mp3/iPod

SONY • APPLE • iRIVER • RIO • DELL

Published by Igloo Books Limited
Henson Way
Telford Way Industrial Estate
Kettering, Northants
NN16 8PX
info@igloo-books.com

This edition published 2005

ISBN 1-84561-155-1

Project Management: **Kandour Ltd**

Author: **Ashley Norris and Katie Lee**
Design and Layout: **Mike Lomax**
Production Management: **Karen Lomax and Kaspa Hazlewood**
Sub Editor: **Colin Dempsey**

Cover image: **With thanks to iRiver. Apple images Courtesy of Apple**

Acknowledgements

Thanks to Chris and especially to Debs and North London's very own two-year-old answer to Nancy Sinatra, Lola.
Ashley

Thanks to Al, Vanessa, Tito and Caroline
Katie

Thanks to:
Apple, Sony, Microsoft, Napster, Belkin, Griffin, Rafe, Philips, PDDrop, iSolio, Creative, Rio, iRiver, Dell, Samsung, Cowon, Oregon Scientific, Ministry of Sound, JVC, Nokia, Sony Ericsson and Sonos.

The authors also wish to thank:
James Snodgrass, Hannah Shepherd, Tim Norris, David Hobbs, Emma Cross, Andrew Burslem, Aimee Lake, Linda Francis, David Murphy, George Cole, Kulwinder Singh Rai, David Phelan, Charlotte Ricca-Smith, Caramel Quin, Simon Munk, Gordon Laing and Gemma Cartwright.

About the authors

Ashley Norris is a London-based freelance journalist and author who has been writing about consumer electronics for longer than he would care to remember. His work is mainly published in *The Guardian* newspaper and UK technology magazines like *T3* and *Total Mobile*.

While writing the book his playlist mainly consisted of *Belle & Sebastian, Thor's Hammer, The Soft Boys* and loads of stuff on *Revola Records*.

Katie Lee is a London-based freelance journalist and author who writes for *The Independent on Sunday* and *Marie Claire* and a host of UK technology magazines. She is also the Editor of *Shiny Shiny* (www.shinyshiny.tv) the first gadget website written for and by women.

While writing the book her playlist mainly consisted of *Morrissey, The Super Furry Animals* and *Pearl Jam*.

Contents

Contents

Contents

Foreword

I remember very clearly the first time that I got to test an MP3 player. It had a very limited storage of just 32MB – enough space for a paltry half hour of tunes. It was also tricky to use and it took me ages to load tracks onto it. Yet at the time I could barely contain my excitement. I imagined that in a few years players like it would allow me to carry round several hours of my favorite tunes – they would be my own personal jukebox that I could carry with me everywhere I went.

Well I was almost right. Within a few years hard disk players capable of storing many hours of music arrived, and then came Apple with its iPod and personal audio players changed forever. The other thing I got wrong was that MP3 would be the de facto future of digital music. Sure the format is still enormously popular, but it has rivals too now in the guise of WMA, AAC and ATRAC and it is hard to say from this juncture which format will establish itself as the dominant within the next few years.

The large number of formats, to say nothing of the huge variety of players, means that the digital audio market is a lot more complex than it really ought to be.

It is my hope that this book goes some way to untangling what can be very complex issues.

If you have already bought an iPod or another player I hope the book proves useful in helping you get getting more out of your personal audio device. If you haven't yet bought a model, hopefully by the end of this book you'll have a few clues as to which model you need.

Ashley Norris

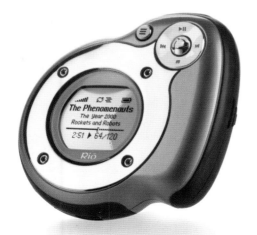

CHAPTER 1

Introduction

Your guide to the digital music revolution

Everything is evolving. Life just doesn't like standing still. Even inanimate objects it seems are not immune, and those fidgety tapes that took ages to rewind did not last long. We are currently in one of those evolutionary leaps when the whole world is going digital so if you don't want to get left behind you'd better get reading.

Introduction
Your guide to the digital music revolution

Every so often a product comes along that changes the world. Back in the 1970s Sony kick- started the personal audio revolution by delivering the cassette tape Walkman. A few years later Sony, in collaboration with Philips unveiled the CD player and the hiss of cassettes and the scratch of vinyl become a thing of the past.

Now we are in the midst of yet another music revolution as CDs are superseded by new digital audio players like the Apple iPod and the Sony NW-HD5.

At the same time people are now becoming as likely to listen to music on their PC as they are on a hi-fi system. And there's even talk of the death of the CD as users download music via the internet to their PC or mobile phone.

The trouble is, as there are many different digital music formats, to say nothing of a host of incompatible players, the new music revolution isn't especially straightforward. The days of simply placing a disc or a tape in a player really have gone forever.

That's why this book exists. In its pages you'll find everything you need to know about the digital music revolution. We'll explain how it all started and offer a few clues as to where it is all going. We'll look at how music arrives on the computer and how you can develop your PC into the type of jukebox you'd always dreamed of owning.

We'll then take apart the players, looking at the incredibly successful iPod series of models from Apple alongside its competitors from the likes of Sony, Philips, Dell and others.

Then you'll finds step by step guides to making the most of the players, in particular, how to get your music on to your computer and then transfer it to

Above:
Sony's NW-HD5 – the iPod's great rival.

Right:
Mini systems with integrated MP3 players are becoming very common now. This Philips model not only hooks up to a portable music player so you can hear the sound through its speakers, it also includes storage for MP3 or WMA tunes.

your chosen device. We'll also take a peek at the huge number of accessories that are available for players like the iPod and the Sony NW-HD5.

Finally we'll wrap it all up by looking at how the digital music player might develop. Will it play video? Will it be part of your mobile phone? We have the answers.

Perhaps you have thought about buying an iPod but were put off because you weren't completely sure how it worked. Or maybe you've already bought a music player and want to know how to make the most of it. Well you have come to the right place.

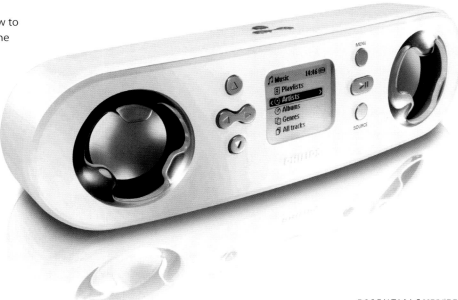

CHAPTER 2

The basics

What is MP3?

Okay let's start with some
basics. What is an MP3 and
how does it work? What are its
rival formats and which of
them will best suit you? Which
format does the iPod use and
why are the different formats
incompatible? How has the
MP3 managed to remain
so popular?

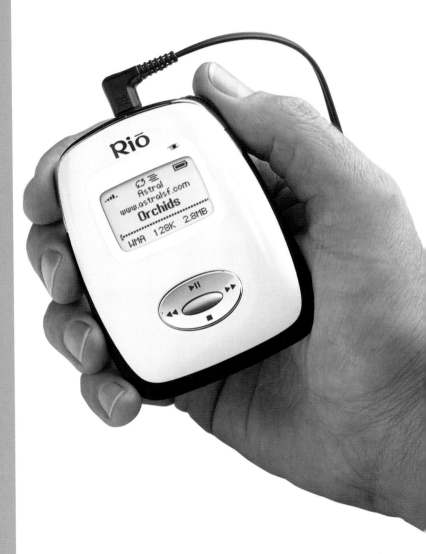

The basics
What is MP3?

You may already have downloaded hundreds of them to your computer, or converted all your CDs to the MP3 format, but even if you've never intentionally bought or created an MP3 file, chances are you'll have at least a couple of MP3 files secreted away somewhere on your PC.

That's because these little files get everywhere. But aside from being the name given to a type of music file, what actually is an "MP3"?

To give it its full name, an MP3 is actually an MPEG-1 Audio Layer 3 file. The MPEG part stands for Moving Picture Experts Group, a group of International Standards created for digitally compressing and coding audio information. Because they're compressed, the MP3 files are far smaller than the full size sound files. MP3 coding reduces files by a factor of 12, which is enough to shrink the music down to a manageable size. This is something that's incredibly important for the internet which was – and still is, though to a lesser extent because of the advent of broadband – governed by issues of bandwidth limits, transfer times and connection speeds.

By taking away any unnecessary parts of the sound signals, the files are compressed without losing too much sound quality. While those with a very trained ear may be able to tell the difference between an MP3 and the original uncompressed version, most people won't be able to discern a huge difference, and the benefits of having smaller, more manageable files make up for a slight drop in quality.

The emergence of the MP3 codec (compression-decompression) made a big difference to the music world. Suddenly there was a file format that was small enough to transfer over the internet, allowing musicians to get their music heard, without having huge resources, providing a new source of revenue to the record labels, and also allowing music fans to share and swap music files. But it may have come as

Previous page:
Rio is one of the longest established MP3 music player brands.

Right:
mp3.com

a surprise to many just how popular the medium became, with the great demand for digital music fuelling a revolution in the way that music is shared and sold.

Unfortunately, this has also led to problems, with many of the record labels – and even some artists – complaining about the unauthorized use and sharing of songs. It's also proved to be a popular scapegoat for the continual decline in single sales.

However, with digital music charts beginning to emerge, and a number of companies realizing the potential of legal digital music sales, MP3, and similar compressed audio formats, set to be around for a long while to come.

Almost all digital music players are compatible with MP3 files and will play them back once they have transferred to the device. The exceptions are older Sony digital music players which feature software that takes the MP3 track and then converts it into another format before it is transferred to the player.

This was a fiddly process and prompted a backlash against Sony. So, following a rethink all Sony models from 2005 onwards will play MP3s back in their existing format.

Of all the digital music files currently available, MP3s

remain the most popular. But there are many other types of music file out there challenging the MP3 for supremacy. These files come in all sorts of different sizes and quality and all of them have been created for different reasons, with issues of compression, encoding rates and digital rights management (copy protection) all coming into play.

The basics
What about the other formats?

WMA

Probably the most well-known format after MP3 is WMA. WMA – or Windows Media Audio – comes to us courtesy of Microsoft. The file sizes tend to be smaller than MP3, offering an encoding rate of 64Kbps that Microsoft claims offers comparable quality to an MP3 coded at 128Kbps.

In effect this should leave you with file sizes that are half the size without halving the quality. But size isn't the only issue, part of the reason Microsoft developed the format is so that protection for copyright could be added.

Digital Rights Management (DRM) can be added to the code of WMA files, which means that companies or individuals that own the rights can keep those rights safe, restricting how and where files are used.

This has meant that WMA has become one of the most popular file format for music download services. Napster, which after Apple's iTunes is arguably the most popular online music store uses WMA as does Microsoft's own MSN service. Although many would argue that the WMA files

consistently offer better sound quality than MP3 – even at the lowest data encoding rates – MP3 continues to hold onto its crown as the most ubiquitous music format.

Part of the reason for that is that not all digital music players will support the WMA format, with many of the largest manufacturers opting to create their own.

You will however find that the vast majority of digital music players are compatible with WMA files. It has been a fixture on PDAs (handheld computers) for quite a while now and is also starting to find its way onto some cellphones too.

Below:
Most digital music players will play back MP3 and Windows Media Audio (WMA) files. Apple players are also compatible with other formats including AAC, while Sony models will play ATRAC files.

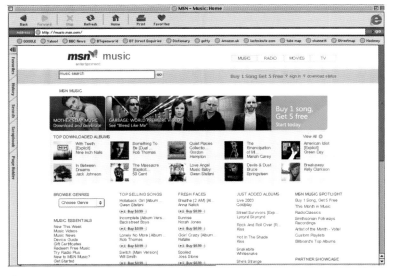

Above:
MSN's music store offers tracks
for legal download in the secure
Windows Media Audio format .

AAC

While Apple didn't actually develop the format, its decision to take up AACs as its favored file type for the iPod music players, has meant that the AAC music file has become synonymous with the players.

AAC is actually a variant of MP3, but offers a more advanced form of file compression. To give it its full name, AAC is more precisely known as MPEG-4 AAC (advanced audio codec).

Although the compression process uses the same theory as MP3's MPEG-1 standard, taking out the sounds that are duplicated and removing data that isn't required, the technique has been refined and improved upon producing smaller file sizes at a higher quality to MP3.

Among the many improvements, AACs offer a larger range of sample frequencies, ranging from 8KHz to 96KHz compared to MP3's 16KHz to 48KHz. This means that the sizes of your music files will be smaller, allowing you to cram more music onto your computers and music players. The coding techniques have also been refined, with more efficient encoding and more efficient treatment of frequency ranges. This should mean that you're left

The basics
What about the other formats?

with a music compression method that produces smaller files at higher qualities. AAC has become one of the most popular music formats in the world thanks mainly to Apple's online iTunes music store. All the music files downloaded from this site are in this format.

Strangely though the number of players compatible with the AAC format is rather limited. Obviously all the Apple models will play back AAC files as will a few other players. There are also some Nokia cellphones that are compatible with AAC files – though not tracks downloaded from the iTunes music store.

The big news for cellphone users is that Motorola has teamed up with Apple to develop a series of phones that not only use AAC but are also compatible with the iTunes music store tracks. Users will download the AAC tracks to their computer and then transfer them on to the phone.

It will be interesting to see how successful the Motorola iTunes phones are and whether they will have any impact on sales of the iPod.

Ogg Vorbis

Ogg Vorbis wins points from many for its open-source status. What this means is that it's free from patents and copyrights, so that anyone can use it without having to pay licensing fees.

The MPEG-based formats all have to be licensed, as does WMA, with the rights holders charging for the codec's use, but Ogg Vorbis is free to anyone.

It uses a similar technique to MP3, removing unnecessary sounds and frequencies that you can't hear anyway, and encoding and compressing sound files to a more manageable size.

It's not entirely the same as MP3, however, and the methods that Ogg Vorbis uses to pick what to dispose of in sound files are viewed as superior to those used by the MP3. This means that an Ogg Vorbis file of the same size as an MP3 should sound better. Alternatively, you can opt to have the same sound quality as an MP3 but at a smaller file size and lower encoding bit-rate.

The number of Ogg compatible players is small, but growing. It is however likely to remain a niche format used mainly by PC-loving geeks for the foreseeable future.

RealAudio

RealAudio is the digital audio format that RealNetworks has come up with.

Unlike Ogg Vorbis' open-source status, RealAudio is, like the formats mentioned previously, a proprietary audio codec that the company developed for use with its RealPlayer. RealAudio files have been designed so that they can be

Below:
Real has its own proprietary format. For more info go to www.real.com

The basics
What about the other formats?

downloaded while you're listening to them. For that reason, they tend to be used a lot by websites, online radio stations and companies seeking to play music on their sites.

In order to allow people to perform live streaming, playing music direct from sites, the RealAudio files need to be very low bandwidths to keep the file sizes down to a minimum.

And because the live streaming RealAudio files can't be saved to your hard drive when they're being offered online via the RealPlayer, they make an ideal option for radio stations and musicians wanting to give people a taste of their music.

However, if you do want people to be able to download your songs to save to a file, the RealAudio format will work with a number of other free players – such as RealAlternative or MPlayer.

Like the other options, RealAudio is considered to offer better quality music in smaller file sizes to the standard MP3 format.

ATRAC

When it comes to music, Sony's not afraid of ploughing its own furrow.

From a company that made the Walkman a household name, and is responsible for one of the world's largest record labels, that's hardly surprising.

ATRAC is the file format that they company came up with to rival MP3 and the various other compression formats. The name stands for Adaptive TRansform Acoustic Coding and it was initially created as a format to encode and compress music onto Sony's MiniDiscs for its portable players.

Although MiniDiscs remain relatively popular (at least in Europe and the Far east) and available, the digital music market has taken a much more determined turn towards flash and hard drive memory players, making removable discs far less vital than they previously were.

And yet that ATRAC format persists. That's because Sony has continued to use it on both its MiniDisc players and on its hard drive and flash music players. The current incarnations of the format are ATRAC3 and ATRAC3plus.

These offer higher quality encoding to MP3 and, like the other alternatives, smaller file sizes. So an ATRAC3plus encoded at 64Kbps should provide the same quality of sound as an MP3 encoded at 128Kbps. While this particular codec is fairly highly rated, the fact that pretty much no one else can play these files – neither software players nor music players – how useful ATRAC us will largely be determined by Sony. Over the past few months there are signs that ATRAC is starting to establish itself as Sony releases players like the NW-HD5 that really can give the Apple iPod a run for its money.

Although it is likely that most owners of the NW-HD5 listen to their music in MP3, they may be adding ATRAC files by downloading them via Sony's online music store Connect.

So far Connect has been a poor cousin of stores like iTunes and Napster, but given Sony's new found enthusiasm for the digital music market, the merger of its music business with BMG (owner of RCA records), and its powerful marketing muscle, you wouldn't bet against Connect becoming a lot higher profile in 2005 and 2006.

Below:
Sony's ATRAC format is one of the most efficient codecs available delivering good quality sound from files that take up little space.

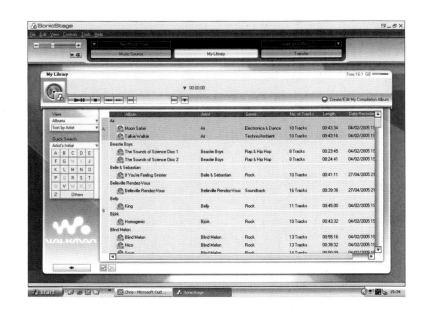

The basics
What about the other formats?

Other Formats

While that may seem like more than enough different codecs to choose from, there are in fact yet more available on the market. Many of them offering similar features and variations on the same themes.

Apple Lossless, for example is Apple's own format, offering uncompressed music files converted from CDs that have no loss of quality, but which are about half the size as standard CD music files.

Liquid Audio files, meanwhile, can be compressed and copyright protected and have been designed especially for use with the Liquid Player.

Above:
MP3 is still the most popular music format largely because it is compatible with so many players including this model from Japanese company NHJ.

Why is MP3 so popular?

Although the market still seems fairly crowded, music compression-decompression formats are still being created and improved upon, helping to keep music quality up and file sizes down. Although many people have their favorites, the general consensus seems to be that pretty much everything else on the market is better than MP3.

So why does it continue to hold the top slot as favored format? Simply because it was first to capture the market and its name is now synonymous with digital audio. In fact, in many cases, people talk about MP3s when in fact they mean WMA, AAC or OGG files, and it has begun to take on a more general meaning, providing a catch-all term for digital music files.

However, it's likely that one, or a couple, of the other digital file types will win out in the end, simply because they offer better quality music at lower file sizes, which is all anyone really wants. Having said that, until there's universal support for any of these alternative codecs, with every music player offering storage and playback of the music files, MP3 is going to remain the easiest format for a lot of users.

CHAPTER 3

Getting started

How to get MP3s on your PC

In this chapter we begin to breakdown the process of transferring music to your computer, whether by ripping CDs or downloading tunes. We show you how to create MP3s and AACs using Apple's iTune's software, and Microsoft Windows Media Audio files and then finally Sony ATRAC files.

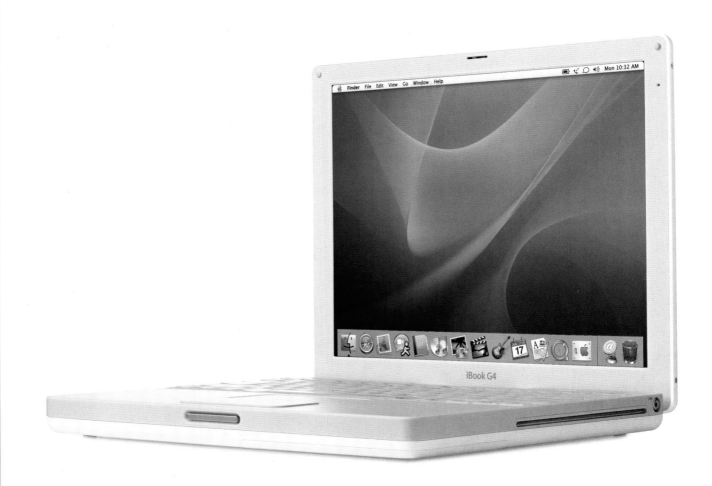

Getting started
How to get MP3s on your PC

You may have just unpacked a bright shiny new iPod, but unless you have any music in either MP3 or AAC formats you will have nothing to play on it. The beauty of music players like the iPod is that they enable you to carry around your entire music collection wherever you go.

Below:
Apple's iTunes is the most popular of all the online music stores and is available to users in both North American and Europe.

That's also their biggest flaw, in that you have to spend time creating digital music files and then transferring them onto the player.

The good news is that while filling, say, a 20 Gigabyte player with 5000 songs is time-consuming, it is also fairly simple to do. The key is getting that music onto your computer in the first place.

Although it is possible to create digital music files and use digital music players with PCs that run older versions of Windows we suspect that the vast majority of users will have either Windows XP, in one of its various formats, or Mac OS 9 or X on their computers.

So over the next few pages we are going to explain very simply how to harness various different types of software to get music files on your PC.

Downloading
or ripping?

Arguably the easiest way of getting music files on to your PC or Mac is by buying them via an online music store. This is a very simple process which is explored in much greater depth in chapter 3. However with individual tracks costing anything up to $1 it can be very expensive to use this method to create a digital music library. Most digital music fans will download tracks from sites, but the vast majority of music on their computers will have been ripped from CDs. For several years now there has been a wide choice of software that enables users to take the PCM (the codec for enconding compact disc music) files on their CDs and convert them in to one of the smaller files (MP3, AAC, WMA) etc which not only takes up much less space on a computer but is also compatible with personal digital music players. Some of the CD rippers you might want to explore include Winamp (www.winamp.com) and Musicmatch (www.musicmatch.com) However for the purpose of this book we are focussing on the three most popular, which, more than coincidentally, happen to be the software which come with the leading players. In other words Apple's iTunes, Microsoft's Windows Media Audio and Sony's SonicStage

Above:
MusicMatch has consistently been one of the most popular MP3 music players/rippers for the PC for several years.

Get started
How to get MP3s on your PC

Creating MP3s/ AACs using iTunes

One of the most praised features of the iTunes software when it was launched originally only for Mac users was that it was easy to use. Fortunately Apple realised that many PC users would want to use iTunes and it rolled out a Windows-friendly version soon after.

Although many iTunes users will own an iPod digital music player you don't need to own one to use the software. You can download the software for free here (www.apple.com/itunes) and the files it creates, if you choose the MP3 options, will play back on almost all digital music players.

The only problem with downloading the software is that for PCs it is quite a big file (around 20MB) so even if you have a broadband connection it will take a few minutes. If you only have a dial up internet connection you may be waiting for some time for it to arrive on your PC.

If you have bought an iPod, adding the iTunes software to your PC is as simple as installing the software via the player's accompanying discs. This will take around ten minutes. Once iTunes is

Above:
Creating MP3s using Apple's iTunes software is a relatively simple process.

installed it will normally display an iTunes icon on your desktop and also in your XP Start button if you are using Windows XP. To get iTunes running you simply click on the icon and it will fire up. Alternatively when you insert a CD into your player it will offer you a series of options. Among these will be play music using iTunes or import songs using iTunes. If you choose the latter then it will automatically start adding the tracks to your music library. If it doesn't it will bring up the iTunes software with the tracks listed.

You then simply click on the import button on the far right hand side of the page and the track will start to be added to your hard disk. An average disc should take no more than five minutes to convert.

Choosing the right format

Before you start importing tracks though you need to instruct the iTunes software on which format to use. To do this open the software and then click on the words 'edit' on the far right of the page. Then choose 'preferences.' This section enables you to optimize the iTunes player in all manner of ways, but the section you need to choose is 'importing'. You then have the choice between storing your music in MP3 or AAC formats, as we explained in chapter one AAC offers better sound quality than MP3, but is only compatible with players from Apple and a few other companies. It might be better to stick to MP3 then if, at a later stage, you swap your Apple player for a device from another manufacturer the tracks will still play back.

You also need to choose the quality settings for the tracks you are storing. Most users opt for good quality (128kbps), which is certainly more than adequate for listening to personal audio players. If you want better sound quality or intend to stream music from the computer around your home, it might be worth considering an even higher bitrate. The trade off though is that the files will be larger and you will get less of them on a personal audio player. In theory you shouldn't have to worry about naming the tracks as you rip them to your computer. The iTunes software

Get started
How to get MP3s on your PC

has a link with a database provided by a company called Gracenote which should work out what your CD is when you place it on the tray and then add the names of the tracks. If you are not online, or for some reason the software doesn't recognize the disc (maybe it is your own compilation CD) you can easily add the name of the tracks yourself.

Once the tracks have been added you can then use the software to order them in many different ways. Another cool feature of iTunes is the way it enables the user to make play lists of their favourite songs. This simply involves creating a new playlist and then dragging and dropping the track in the new folder. These playlist can easily be exported to an iPod too.

If you own Mac then there isn't really a huge difference between how things work on Windows PCs and how things work on Macs, in terms of how the software works. Similarly to Windows you can set iTunes to automatically add tunes from a CD to your library when you insert a disc into your computer.

You also get a choice of AAC or MP3 and you can select the various bitrates to choose between the quality levels you require. If you choose a lower bitrate you can fit more songs on your player. If you choose a higher bitrate you can store a smaller number of songs, but at a better sound quality.

One rather neat recent addition to iTunes software is duplication facility. If you even have more than one version of the same song in your iTunes library (say you have it on an original album and a greatest Hits) you just choose "Find duplicates" from the Edit menu, and iTunes will display all the duplicate songs in your music library, making it very easy for you to decide which of the duplicates you might want to delete.

Below:
Transferring tracks from your PC or your Mac to an iPod is a fast and simple process with most albums taking just a few seconds.

Creating Windows Media Audio (WMA) files

If you have just bought a new PC running Windows XP included with the package is digital music software for the computer called Windows Media 10. If your PC is slightly older it may have an earlier version of the software. If it does it is well worth visiting here (www.microsoft.com/windows /window smedia/mp10/default.aspx) to download version 10 as it has some cool new features.

Like iTunes it is large file and will take a few minutes to download if you have broadband, a lot longer if you are using a dial up internet connection.

Microsoft has made it simple to add new content to your PC too. When you put a CD in your disc drive to transfer all the tracks to the hard disk involves one press of the 'Rip' button at the top of the screen.

You can also choose which music format you want to use – Windows Media or MP3? And again decide what quality you want the file to be.

To do this click on 'Rip', and then go to 'Tools' and then 'Options', and then finally 'Rip music'.

Below:
If you have bought a new Windows XP PC it will come with Windows Media Player 10. If you have an older version it is well worth upgrading.

Get started
How to get MP3s on your PC

Ripping CDs using SonicStage

Also along the top are other clearly labelled 'action' buttons. So again with one click you can 'Burn' some tracks to a CD, explore your library of music or access Internet radio stations.

Another key enhancement is the way which Windows Media 10 has over its predecessors is the way it links up with all kinds of media providers. So, for example, if you want to download a new track or an album you can do so legally via the MSN Music (www.msn.com) site or alternatively Napster (www.napster.com). Both offer high quality versions of tracks in the Windows Media Audio (WMA) format.

There are advantages of encoding all your music in WMAs especially as WMA files will play back in a large number of personal audio devices as well as PDAs and some cellphones. If you want to stick with tracks that can be ported on any device through opt for an MP3.

At the time of writing Windows Media 10 was not yet available for Macs, though this of course could change very shortly. Mac users can however download Windows Media 9.

SonicStage is the software developed by Sony and bundled with its range of digital music players. Initially it got bad reviews with users arguing that it was difficult to negotiate, though fortunately for Sony and its fans the latest version of the software is much more straightforward.

SonicStage works in a similar way to both Windows Media 10 and iTunes. Again if you have the software running it can automatically import all the tracks each time you put a CD in the tray.

The only key difference is that you can only choose between Sony's ATRAC format (see chapter one) or WAV which is the format the CD was originally stored in as a very large file. If you don't think you will stick with Sony players ATRAC

It might be better though to use either iTunes or Windows Media 10 to create MP3 files and as these will still be able to transfer easily to all 2005 Sony digital audio players. The big advantage of using ATRAC is that you can get MP3-quality tunes using lower bitrates. In practice this means you can squeeze more tunes on your personal audio player.

Another benefit is that the battery on Sony players last longer if they are playing ATRAC tunes rather than MP3 ones, so for example the NW-HD5 will run for 40 hours with ATRAC files and 30 hours with MP3s.

Left:
Only use Sony's SonicStage software to rip CDs if you are confident that you will only buy Sony music players.

CHAPTER 4

Downloading

Where it all began

Now let's turn our full attention to downloading. We'll show you how to get started, how to download from Apple's iTune's Music Store and Sony's Connect service and other music download servers.

Downloading
Where it all began

The origins of music downloading lie in the early internet community. In the 1990s most online music was put there by teenagers and college students with no regard for copyright issues.

But finding these files was relatively difficult, and users had to be fairly committed to seeking out music on USENET groups and Lycos searches if they wanted to take advantage of illegal file sharing.

Then, in 1999, Shawn Fanning decided to set up a more organized method of sharing music and Napster was born. The company was the first of its kind, offering users the opportunity to upload and download MP3s to each other's machines. It didn't take long for the lawsuits to start rolling in, the first one arriving that year from the RIAA (Recording Industry Association of America).

Despite this, Napster continued to provide the service, and more sprang up like it, including Kazaa and Audiogalaxy. These services have been blasted by record companies, and even some musicians have stepped in to condemn the theft of their music.

Peer-to-peer

Some file-sharing services are "peer-to-peer", which means that files are directly transferred from one computer to another without using a central server to upload to and download from. Users have to be online at the same time to do this, and using this technique means that computers can take advantage of shared bandwidth. Napster used peer-to-peer in a slightly different way, keeping some data on servers to create a search database, and using direct peer-to-peer for the actual file transfers.

Eventually, however, Napster had to bow down to the pressure from lawsuits, and the company has now gone legitimate, offering a legal downloads service that continues to be unmatched by other online downloads stores.

The high profile nature of its various court cases, most notably from rock band Metallica and pop star Madonna in 2000, served as good publicity for the company, which had previously been frequented only by the most web savvy customers (the geek community). Since then, it has quickly established itself as one of the most popular and comprehensive download libraries and is used by people from all walks of life and all levels of

Above:
MP3.com is one of the
longest running online
music services.

Downloading
Getting started

technical experience. Its full services will be explored in the next chapter.

While Napster has opted to take the legal route, eschewing its shady origins, there remain a number of file sharing services that continue to occupy the attentions of record labels, artists and copyright protectors. Kazaa has managed to stay online, despite many lawsuits, funding itself through inbuilt adware on downloads.

After being sued by the RIAA Audiogalaxy decided to stop running its original service, and instead licensed the Rhapsody service that Real also uses.

It continues to offer the same online community feel as it did before, providing assistance to new record labels and bands wanting to get their music heard and offering a forum for music fans and musicians to communicate.

As well as these early illegal sites, companies such as Real, Apple and Sony have offered their own downloads sites, each one coming up with different features, artists and file types to entice the customers.

Getting started

So what do you need to get to start downloading music off the internet? Firstly, you need to decide which music player or software you want to use to play your songs on, and then you can pick the download service accordingly.

Apple uses an AAC file format, Sony works with its own ATRAC file compression technology, Real offers a number of different formats including WMA and AAC, while Napster uses WMA files. If you want to take advantage of Napster's subscription service (see the next chapter for details) you'll need to make sure that you have one of the compatible players from the likes of iriver, Creative, Samsung and Gateway. For Apple's iTunes, meanwhile, you'll have to opt for one of Apple's own players (for a full run down of Apple's range see Chapter 6).

You also need to bear in mind that none of the stores has access to every single track out there. Despite being one of the most comprehensive sites, for example, even Apple has some pretty well-known bands missing. That's all down to the various agreements and deals signed by the record labels, and it's likely that, for the larger stores at least, any gaping holes will be filled as time goes on.

Once you've found the right player and music site for you, you'll need to download the software that lets you buy, play and organize tracks on your computer. Many of these have a minimum requirement.

Napster's service, for example, needs Windows 2000 or above and will not run on the Mac OS. In terms of power requirements for your computer, you'll find that so long as you have a relatively up-to-date machine, you won't have any trouble running the software.

Because you're downloading data from the internet, you'll also need to make sure that your connection speeds can handle the transfer.

It's not imperative that you get broadband, but you will find that this provides a more reliable and speedy download service. If you lost connection halfway through a download, you will have to start all over again so make sure that you can get continuous connection during the transfer.

Above:
Napster's online music library consists of over a million tracks.

Downloading
Using iTunes

Using iTunes

Apple is well-known for producing products that are plain and simple to use and the iTunes software and online shop iTunes Music Store (ITMS) are no different. Download the 21MB application to your computer and Apple's Rendezvous technology will automatically look for any music files, no matter where they are, and display them all in one place for you. This makes it an incredibly simple introduction to digital music for those not well versed in it.

The application looks very clean and simple too, with a basic style and layout that makes it feel readily accessible. Whereas some of these music library/music player applications are littered with a vast array of buttons and information, Apple has kept iTunes free from clutter, in keeping with the minimalist designs of the iPods.

Importing tunes that you already have saved to your hard drive is nice and easy, and organizing tracks into playlists and groups can be done simply from the menu lists and on-screen side bar. In fact, the "Smart Playlists" option will automatically create playlist for you, allowing you to organize all your tunes into groups such as "90s Music" or "25 Most Played". The iTunes set up also comes with Apple's shuffle feature, which will play tunes randomly from your playlist. Of course, it's not a new concept, and other music players have included it before, but by making it one of the iTunes and iPod players' central features, it has become associated with Apple.

iTunes Music Store

Just as playing music is easy and straightforward on iTunes, Apple has tried to make purchasing music as practical as possible, allowing you to access the online shop from your iTunes software.

Simply click on the "iTunes Music Store" link on the left-hand folder sidebar and the site will appear within the player software.

Although you may be used to using your preferred internet browser to explore the web, this really is a

more simplified way of navigating the store –
buttons are kept to a minimum and since all of
them are related to iTunes, there's no way you can
accidentally navigate away from the site or lose
your place.

You can always get back to the home screen, and
can always move back and forwards within the site.
This means your purchases can be accomplished in
a very short space of time.

Rather than simply listing all the thousands of tracks
and albums in the iTunes catalogue, Apple has
made the home screen as appealing as possible
tothose who just want to browse.

Suggested playlists from celebrities are on offer,
while Apple itself has sorted a number of tunes into
compilation albums – such as "air guitar music" or
"love songs".

Obviously, you don't have to purchase the whole
album of tracks and individual numbers can be
picked out of the selection, but having suggested
tunes for you to check out means you may find

Above:
The iTunes music store is
available in much of Europe
and North America.

Downloading
Using iTunes

something you'd forgotten about or always wanted to hear. There are also pictures of the latest albums added to the catalogue and recommended titles.

The sides of the shop front, meanwhile, are filled with all sorts of other information. On the ride side panel you'll find a run down of the day's most popular singles and albums, along with a small selection of promotional tracks that are free to download. On the left side you'll find links to even more celebrity playlists and recommended listens, links that let you browse music by genre, and a selection of different charts, including billboard and singles.

You'll also be able to access information about purchasing pre-paid cards and gift certificates, setting up an allowance that you or a member of your family can spend each month, and starting a search for a particular track, album or artist.

Searching
for music

At the very top of your iTunes application, in the silver bar, you'll see a white field with a magnifying glass in it. This is the quick search option, which lets you type in the name of a song, album or artist to find the band or song you're after. If that doesn't prove detailed enough, you can opt to run a Power Search, which can be accessed by clicking on the link on the left hand side panel.

If you go into the search section you'll see that there are a number of fields you can fill in to narrow your search down.

To run a search for all the songs by a particular band or artist, simply fill in the artist or band's name and all the tracks held on the iTunes store should appear. You'll also be given details of a couple of the latest or best selling albums and a list of the most popular downloads for that group or artist.

If you decide to buy an entire album, you can then just click on the arrow by the title to go to a page dedicated to the album. This will give you a list of the most popular downloads, suggested additional songs you might like to consider, and "Album Notes"

with information about the recordings and often a review. Alternatively, for more information about the band itself, you can click on the arrow next to the band name to go to a special artists page.

Often, this will provide you with a wealth of information, including a biography of the band or artist, and a full list of the albums available – although details like these will be limited for smaller, less well-established bands and artists. It's worth noting that running a search for a band or artist sometimes doesn't bring up every single album or song available.

If you're having trouble finding what you want, clicking through to the artist's dedicated page should allow you to hunt out the album or tune you're after.

Although iTunes is a very well laid out shop, the search tools are by no means infallible. If you're finding it hard to get hold of the song or band you're after, it's worth running a few different types of search, going in to the actual artist's page, or simply browsing through the musical genre categories.

Downloading
Using Sony Connect

Making the purchase

You'll need to have an account with iTunes if you want to purchase tracks.

Click on the Sign In button near the top of the screen and you can create an account there. Setting it up doesn't take long – just fill in your personal details and credit/debit card information. Once you've got all this information on your account, you can login to the site automatically each time you visit from your computer.

Then you can simply click on the track you want to buy and the song will be downloaded to your iTunes folder on your computer without you having to go to the trouble of adding card details every time. Because this is all done over a secure connection, there's no need to worry about other people being able to gather your personal details or credit card number for their own use.

A receipt will be emailed to you to confirm that you've made the purchase and you'll be able to listen to the track instantly and save it to your iPod. Tracks are reasonably cheap at $0.99 (£0.79 in the UK) – though that's by no means the cheapest

option around – but it's worth remembering that Apple uses Digital Rights Management so you can't just do whatever you want with the tracks.

You will be able to save songs onto CDs, but you can't then copy them over to someone's computer without first verifying your password and login details – and you'll only be able to do that with 5 computers. You can, however, share songs over a local area network in your home or office, allowing anyone on the network to play – but not copy – the tunes on the server.

Below:
Once you have downloaded the song you store it on your computer, burn it on to CD and transfer it to a portable player.

Introducing
Sony Connect

The actual SonicStage software and Sony Network Walkman players will be explored in later chapters, but if we're talking about downloading tracks from Sony Connect it's worth pointing out here that the company only currently sells its own ATRAC3 files for use on the players, so you're limited to buying tracks from the Sony Connect store, or transferring music from your CDs into ATRAC format.

Even the MP3s that Sony has finally agreed to support need to be run through the SonicStage music library to ensure that you can't copy or save them to more than 3 other computers. This means that, at 99 cents per track, you won't be able to do much with your music if you decide to stop using Sony players and want to try out something different.But that's pretty much what you get from Apple as well and since the Sony Network Walkman players are so well made and designed, you may find yourself happy to stick with them for the long term anyway. Unfortunately, you can't currently play tunes from SonicStage through a network, so you won't be able to share tracks with work colleagues or family members.

You are also limited on how many times you can burn tunes to CD. You can burn each tune up to 10 times, but 5 of those times have to be onto ATRAC CDs, which means they'll only work on Sony CD players. And though you can copy tracks to three other computers (which you'll need to register with Sony Connect along with your music players), only the main computer has the authority to burn CDs or copy music to portable players.

Using
Sony Connect

Unlike Apple you don't have to access the Sony Connect store through your SonicStage software if you don't want, and can get shopping straight on your internet browser. Having said that, since you'll need the SonicStage software on your computer to organize, transfer and play tracks anyway, you might find it just as simple to go through this software to access the shopfront. Getting SonicStage is free and although it's a reasonably big file, at 36MB, it's easy

Downloading
Other online music stores

enough to download and install. While you're setting it all up, it's worth changing the location of your music directory as the standard setting hides the folder away in some hard to find location otherwise.

The actual Connect store was criticized on its launch for being clunky and difficult to navigate. It also looked as if it was only half finished in the early months, with photos missing and a number of glitches on the pages.

Now it's had time to mature, the site is looking far more appealing, with a nice enough design that has the same album highlight adverts in the center of the screen as iTunes, with the menu lists and search engines located on the sides.

As with iTunes you can browse by genre or run a full search for artist, track or album title. The right side displays album and singles charts information.

Sony also provides music news and gossip on the home page. These small snippets of stories won't provide you with a great deal of information, but the headlines often grab your interest, taking you further into the store. How much that affects your purchase is unclear, and Sony lacks the slickness of iTunes. There are no celebrity playlists, for instance,

and although you'll find featured artists and featured genres, it's no where near as plentiful as iTunes, and it's far less likely to get you browsing for tunes or checking out new types of music.

This isn't a problem if you just want to buy a particular track, and with over 700,000 tracks to pick from you get a reasonable amount of choice, but it's far harder to use it for general browsing than iTunes.

Although many of the flaws with the site design have been ironed out, it still runs surprisingly sluggishly. Performing a search for bands can take an age, with pages often refreshing at a very slow pace. Once you find the tracks you're after, you can listen to 30-second snippets to check they're the right ones, or get a taster of what they sound like. Alternatively, you can stick it straight into your shopping cart.

Unlike iTunes, which downloads tracks as soon as you log in and click "Buy", Sony uses the more traditional online shopping set up, with a shopping cart and checkout.

If you've already entered your card details you'll be able to buy tracks instantly, with the tunes downloading to your SonicStage music folder.

Other sites

In both the United States and the UK there are now a host of other sites offering legal music downloads. Some are completely independent, while others are linked to internet Service providers (ISPs).

Almost all use Windows Media Audio files and most have smaller selections than either iTunes or Napster. In the US, MSN's site www.msn.com is one of the biggest, while in the UK companies look at Tiscali's Music Club (www.tiscali.co.uk/music) and MyCokeMusic (www.mycokemusic.com).

There are also a couple of sites which use MP3, the most high profile of which is Wippit in the UK (www.wippit.co.uk). This is also now available in the US (www.wippit.com).

CHAPTER 5

Napster

The online jukebox

In which we introduce Napster and demonstrate how Napster turns your PC into a jukebox and how easy it is to transfer Napster files on to your music player.

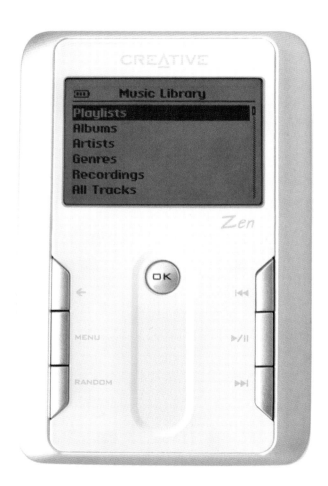

Napster
The online jukebox

Napster holds a special place in the history of digital music for a number of reasons. Firstly, because in its pioneering – though it ought to added – illegal period, it popularized MP3 file swapping. More importantly, though, it is special because of the number of innovations it has developed during its couple of years as a legitimate site.

For while Napster holds a huge library of music which can be downloaded in the traditional way like other sites such as iTunes and Connect, it also boasts some fairly unique features which are worth exploring in a little more detail.

The legitimate version of Napster first launched in the US in 2003 as www.napster.com. Since then it has expanded its reach across the globe with the UK Napster (www.napster.co.uk) and Canada (www.napster.ca) following in 2004.

Drop into one of the Napster sites and at first glance it doesn't appear to be that different from its rivals. It is only when you start to delve deeper that you notice the site's unique selling points.

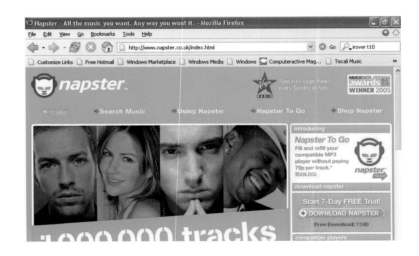

Three Napster Options

There are three very different ways in which you can use Napster. Firstly if it is only specific tracks that you are after that you want to download to your music player or possibly to a CD then you need to look at the Napster Light facility.

You will need to download the Napster software to your PC. You'll also need to ensure that you are using Microsoft's Windows Media Player seven or higher.

Once you have done this you have an application on your desktop which will open when you click on it. You'll then see pages, not unlike iTunes or Connect, that offer all kinds of music for you to download.

At the time of writing the figure was over a million tracks in the US and UK (700,000 in Canada), but in reality it may be getting towards double that figure by the time you read this.

If you know the name of the track or the artist you can do a quick search for them. Alternatively you can choose the catalogue of tunes by artist, by type of music, or even by the various specialist charts.

Once you have found what you want you can

Above:
Napster has over a
million tracks available
for download from its
US music store.

Napster
Napster To Go

normally stream a thirty second clip of the track to work out whether or not you like it. If you want to buy it you just click the 'buy now download' button.

You'll pay 99c in the US and 79p in the UK. If you want to buy whole albums it obviously works out little cheaper. Napster uses Windows Media Audio files. You need to be a little careful about which player you own, as while most player are compatible with WMA files, not all will play the copyright protected versions. As a general rule of thumb models from Samsung, Creative and Rio work fine. There's a list of players on the Napster site if you aren't sure whether yours will work.

Napster as a jukebox

If you ever want to delve deeper into Napster you should consider a subscription to its jukebox service. For $9.95 or £9.95 in the UK, this allows you to stream any track from the Napster online library via your computer. So should you fancy hearing an old Bruce Springsteen track you haven't heard in ages or maybe you want to check out a new band for downloading their music or buying their CD you can.

The service turns your PC into the world's biggest jukebox and, as the number of tracks online grows so does your jukebox.

If you have a party coming you can use the service to create a playlist of your favourite tracks and when the evening begins you just press play and the music starts. All this without having to download a track.

Napster To Go

Napster's most recent innovation takes its home streaming facility and sends it out with you. Napster To Go enables you to take any of the tracks on the online server, download them to your PC and then take them with you on your personal digital audio player.

It works as subscription with you paying $14.95 month in the US, or £14.95 a month in the UK. You then download the software and away you go. You also do need to have a Napster To Go music player. These are a littler thin on the ground at the moment, but do include several models from Creative and Rio. You will also need to have downloaded Windows Media 10 player as the service doesn't work with any of the previous versions of this software.

Once you have your subscription then fill up the player with as many tracks as you want. However if you unsubscribe the tracks then become unplayable leaving you with no music on your device.

The service is relatively simple to use. Your player pops up on the interface and then you move tracks on to the device via your PC. It takes roughly around the same time to transfer a track from Napster as it does downloading and moving a track from one of its rival services.

If you aren't sure which track you want to download one handy feature is the option of browsing other member's collections. This allows you to see what they are listening to, and if you find someone with similar musical taste to your own you can simply transfer their choice of tracks to your player.

Napster To Go is certainly an innovative way of filling a music player, and in some ways it is ideal for newbies who might not have many MP3s, or don't want to spend a lot of money downloading individual tracks. The subscription for Napster To Go also covers the streaming service too, so if you are interested in music and want to have access to a huge library both at home and on the move it is well worth giving the service a spin.

Below:
If you cancel your subscription the Napster To Go tracks on your portable players simply won't play any more.

CHAPTER 6

What type of player?

Hard disk or flash?

Not sure which type of player to purchase? We're here to help. We'll introduce you to flash players and show you the key features

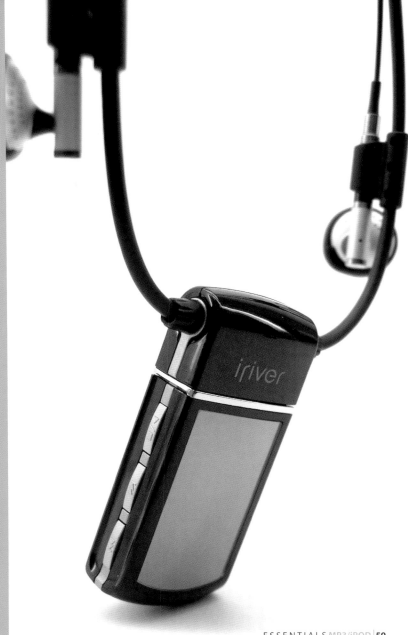

What type of player
Hard disk or flash?

With the emergence of digital music and music downloading came the advent of the digital music player. With so many sound files available to buy, having somewhere to play them became very important.

Being able to listen to and create digital music on your computer is all very well, but if you want a bit of musical accompaniment as you go about your day, portable players are the way to.

Although many portable CD players began offering support for digital music playback, having to copy your music onto CD and carry round a large CD player defeated the object of having MP3s in the first place.

Flash Players

Flash memory seemed like the obvious solution for portable digital music playback. Used for many years in memory cards, PDAs and other forms of portable storage, the technology was well established and readily available to develop flash

players. Flash memory is a non-volatile memory type, which means that data stored on it should be less vulnerable to loss. Data is stored on chips, which means that once you have saved something it won't be lost even when you switch the device off. It also has the benefit of requiring no moving parts, so that you don't have to suffer the problems of music skipping or jogging as you move about.

Players using flash memory are small and lightweight, but this can have disadvantages as well. The reason they can be so small is because the actual memory capacity is comparatively small. So if you were planning on keeping your entire music collection on one player you should probably think again. Larger sizes are being developed, but they still have a way to go before they can compete with the memory power of hard drive players. But what they lack in memory power, they more than make

Above:
Nike teamed up with Dutch company Philips to pioneer a really good range of flash memory based players for joggers and sports enthusiasts.

Right:
The iPod shuffle, which launched in early 2005, is now the most popular flash memory based player in the world.

up for in size and portability. For those wanting some music on their daily commute, or a soundtrack to their daily run, these players are so easy to just pop in a pocket, or hang off a neck chain. And while the very largest size can get expensive, the smaller players are now extremely affordable, making them highly accessible players for everyone.

Features of Flash Players

When they first emerged onto the market, these little players were fairly basic, ran on standard batteries and needed rather fiddly installation procedures in order to get them working. Now the flash player market is becoming far more sophisticated, with players that have broadened their horizons and offer all sorts of extra features and facilities. Because of their flash-based memory, using them as external storage devices for your computer and laptop is nothing new, but many of them are now more geared up to work as storage devices, mimicking the design of standard memory keys, and including a full size USB connector built in that can be plugged straight into your computer's USB port. This is something that Apple has done with its latest iPod

shuffle player, but companies such as Creative with its earlier Muvos have been doing it for a while.

Those sorts of players also have the benefit of being plug and play which means you don't need to install software to get them running on your computer. This makes them far more practical for moving music and other data directly from one computer to another. They also tend to make transferring data easy, with many of them providing drag and drop operability - so you can just drag music and other data straight from your hard drive folders into the flash drive.

Another secondary feature that has proved popular is voice recording. If you need to record a lot of meetings, take interviews, or even just record your own notes and reminders, many of the smaller flash players include an in-built mic and voice recording facility. Having a portable digital voice recorder to hand at all times is a real boon for many.

The inclusion of an FM radio tuner is a cheap and easy option for many of the flash player creators, and because they have limited storage space, it adds a bit of extra music potential when you have run out of your chosen tracks. Some players even include a radio record facility, which means you can save songs and shows straight onto your flash player when you're out and about simply by hitting the record button.

What type of player
Types of flash player

Flash Future

Jewelry

The extreme versatility of the flash format has led to digital music players being included in the unlikeliest of places. As well as support for MP3 on digital cameras and camcorders, you can also now find MP3 playing wrist watches from companies like Evergreen and Lax. Players are also being created to double up as jewelry, so that iriver's N10 can be worn as a necklace pendant, the screen turning into a silver mirror-like surface when the player is off. BenQ also makes a pendant player, the Joybee 102r, while many of the new players, the iPod shuffle included, have been designed to be worn either round the neck or strapped round your arm. Oakley, meanwhile, has taken the concept even further and come up with a pair of sunglasses, the Oakley Thump MP3 shades.

Sports

Because you don't get any skipping or jogging on flash players they've become associated with sports and running. Players such as the Nike-Philips psa128max are incorporated into pedometers for runners and walkers, and most companies produce a player with rubberized casing and protection for

Left:
Sony has been making flash memory based players for half a decade now. The latest models combine good looks with exceptional battery life.

Right:
Rio Audio also has a solid range of flash memory based players most of which are noted for their excellent quality screens.

defense against any knocks and drops. Waterproof players are also starting to spring up such as the SwiMP3 from Finis Inc and Oregon Scientific's MP120. These are still pretty rare, but more have started to appear in recent months.

Screens

By their very nature, flash players' main strengths lie in their small sizes. For this reasons the screens on them tend to be very small, usually non-color and fairly basic. Indeed, Apple's iPod shuffle has done away with the screen altogether, resulting in a more affordable player and a more straightforward set up. Not all companies are taking this route, however, and color screens are starting to appear on flash players, including the newer high quality, lower power OLED (Organic Light Emitting Diode) screens. For many, this is seen as an improvement in usability (although the popularity of the shuffle suggests that a fair proportion of consumers think otherwise), and while flash players aren't quite taking on the likes of the iPod photo and other color screen music players, some of them, such as NHJ's VP712B, can be used for storing and viewing your digital images.

Sizes

Being able to carry round personal data like music files and photos, in such a small format, makes flash players very attractive to consumers, and it seems that hardly a month goes by without someone

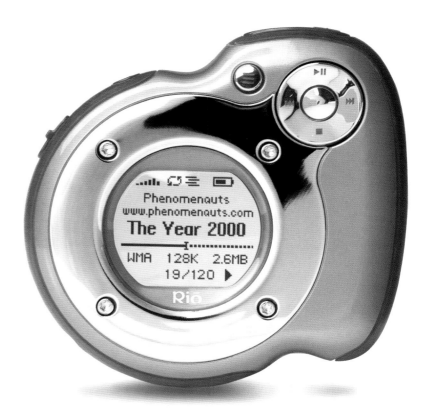

What type of player
Hard disk models

announcing the "world's smallest MP3 player".
BenQ, Samsung, Oregon Scientific and MobiBlu have
all taken their turn claiming to have created the
smallest – and it seems an obsession that these
companies are likely to continue -– all of them vying
for the "world's smallest" title. But the small size
means you're stuck with smaller memory size and
often flash players can be seen as more trouble than
they're worth. Unless you're happy to listen to the
same couple of albums over and over, you'll soon
grow tired of your music selection. One potential
solution is the addition of Bluetooth, a feature of the
NHJ VP712B, which means that you can send new
tracks to your player straight from your computer
without having to worry about connecting it all up
with wires. But if you need larger storage capacities
together with the skip free performance that flash
can offer, you'll be glad to know that flash sizes are
increasing all the time, with the very latest players to
appear including up to 2GB of storage.

Trouble is, players such as the Cowon G3 2GB
model cost far more than a hard drive player and
offer nowhere near the storage space.

Hard Drive Players

Flash may offer you a reliable, non-volatile, non
jumping music player, but if you want to get serious
with your digital music and covert all your CDs to
music files, you'll need to get something that's a bit
more roomy for holding your collection. That's
where hard drive players come in. These storage
devices tend to be far larger than flash players, but
they offer considerably more space, with current
digital jukeboxes offering storage up to 60GB.

Music hard drives really aren't that far removed from
the hard disk drives you find in your computers and
laptops, and it's from this technology that portable
external hard drives started to emerge.

These were initially designed simply to allow you a
back up for your computer, or for a bit of extra
storage capacity when you needed it. From there,
portable hard drives started to develop which
offered a bit more functionality, with the likes of
Archos and Creative creating their music jukeboxes.

And, ever since, the format has grown and grown
until we get to where we are today – a market filled
with a huge selection of hard drive players with

every variety of color and design offering us the opportunity of packing away our CD collection and relying on one small, portable unit to keep all our music on.

Memory Melt Down

But are we right to abandon our CD collection in favor of this one box solution for music storage? Sure, it's more convenient to just plug your hard drive into your stereo and leave it to keep playing all day long, but what about the reliability of hard drives? If you've ever had a computer hard drive fail on you, you'll know the terrible experience of losing all your data – all your work, music and photos. Hard disk drives are made from many spinning parts and memory is based on magnetic technology rather than the non-volatile chip memory of flash players. This means that a serious knock or drop could damage all your music irretrievably, or the hard drive could simply stop spinning one day. But it's not all doom and gloom. The fact is, no memory source is ever one hundred per cent safe from data loss and as long as you have all your music backed up somewhere – even if it's only in its original CD

Below:
Hard disk based models generally boast much storage than flash players enabling users to store image and video files as well as music.

What type of player
Hard disk picture players

form, or digitally on your computer – chances are you'll never have a day's trouble. And the far larger sizes you get from a hard drive player makes any of these concerns seem less important – after all, being able to get all your music in one place, and at the touch of a button, is a highly appealing prospect. Having a hard drive player that's still small enough to be portable means you'll never be short of music.

Hard Drive Evolution
While the beauty of flash is its versatility – the fact that you can stick it in nearly any shape of device – hard drives are slightly more controlled by the restraints on hard drive sizes and shapes. But since their inception, hard drive manufacturers such as Hitachi and Seagate have been working hard to get the format as small and lightweight as possible, whilst at the same time pushing the memory capacities to greater sizes. In the space of just a few years, for example, the iPod range from Apple has got slimmer and slimmer, yet more and more capacious. The first iPod in 2001 had a capacity of 5GB, and was considerably heavier than today's models, which start with a 20GB capacity. Meanwhile, at the top end, you can now get players with 60GB of memory and it doesn't look likely to end there: 80GB and 120GB players are a very real possibility for the future. So

flash players have got a long way to go before they can challenge the hard drive market, and in spite of the increased potential for music loss and track skipping, the sheer size of the storage capacities and their relative affordability, means hard drive players are going to be around for a long while to come.

Photo Players

Just because the hard drive format is less flexible than the flash format, it doesn't mean there aren't plenty of opportunities for adding extra features. Voice recording is a popular addition and FM radio has been cropping up more and more on recent models. But it's for photo storage that the hard drive models really comes into their own. They may have been conceived simply as portable music devices, but the huge increase in digital photography and the ballooning size of hard drive capacities has made hard disk players the obvious solution for photo storage. Apple recognized this with the launch of the iPod Photo range, which comes with a larger-than-average color screen for showing friends and family your photo slideshows.

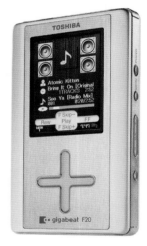

Above:
Toshiba's Gigabeat models are noted for their excellent sound quality and superb color screens.

Right:
Apple's iPod photo is the most popular color screen player available. Its owners can use it to see artwork of music downloaded from iTunes as well as their own snaps.

But it's the not the only company to take advantage of color screens, with players such as iRiver's H10 and Archos' Gmini 400 including displays big enough for checking out your images.

Multimedia Players

Why stop at music and photos when today's hard drives are more than up to the task of powering complete portable entertainment systems? Portable media players based on Microsoft's own Portable Media Center operating system, or ones that run on their own software are becoming more popular, especially as the digital video market begins to pick up. The players themselves are still pretty large, and only those seeking entertainments on long journeys, or real film and TV addicts are going to opt to carry one in place of a standard music player. But the larger screens and, in some cases, advanced functionality make them a tempting prospect for many, and they are certainly a development worth watching. It seems inevitable that players like these are the future for hard drive storage (should the legal download of film and television programs become a possibility) we'll be exploring them in Chapter 20.

CHAPTER 7

Apple

Enter the iPod

If you've ever wondered where the iPod came from and how Apple has kept it one step ahead of the rivals, we have the answers.

Apple
Enter the iPod

It is a common misconception that Apple invented the MP3 player market. While the company may boast the most popular and iconic of all digital music players it certainly wasn't there first.

The earliest player was in fact a basic 32MB flash memory (it held about half an hour of music) model made by Saehan, the MPMan, which went on sale in spring 1998. Ironically it was about the same size as the current 20 Gigabyte iPod.

Apple wasn't even the first company to produce a hard disk player either. That accolade belongs to the Hango/Remote Solutions Personal Jukebox PJB-100, which came out in 1999.

 Apple wasn't even the first big maker to offer a hard disk player. Its big rival Creative arguably popularized the hard disk player with its Jukebox a year later.

What Apple has achieved with the iPod, in its various incarnations, is it to take digital music players out of the preserve of music die-hards and computer-loving geeks and deliver them to the mainstream. Apple has managed this by utilizing its core strengths of excellent design, simplicity of use, and superb marketing.

Quite how much longer Apple will continue to dominate the music playing market is a subject of fierce debate. There's no doubt that, in terms of the players it offers, Sony has caught up, and some argue even over taken its great rival.

Other commentators believe that the iPod will be eclipsed by the mobile phone as users listen to music on handsets like the Nokia N91 which boasts a four Gigabyte hard disk.

Apple fans point to the fact that each time a rival has got close to its players the company has delivered an even more amazing product.One thing Apple's critics can't deny though and that is that at the moment the company is dominating the music playing market by offering a superb range of music players that work seamlessly with the world's most popular online music store.

Over the next few pages we are going to look in detail at Apple and its range of models. We'll whiz back briefly and look at how the iPod established itself as the most popular hard disk music player and how Apple has maintained that momentum by offering the mini, photo and the shuffle.

We'll focus on how you go about using the iPods, and offer hints and tips on how to get the best out of the players. Finally we'll take a tour through the huge number of accessories now on sale for the Apple, players.

If you are thinking about buying an iPod, this is the place to start.

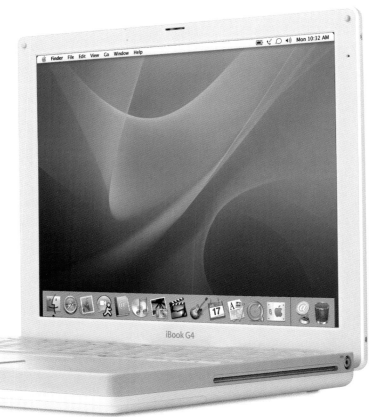

The standard iPod

Apple's success story

In this chapter we'll take you through the evolution of the iPod, from the time the world went iPod crazy to the future of the iPod and speculation on what future players will be like. We'll tell you why you should buy one, how to use it and give you hints and tips on how to make the most of the player.

The standard iPod
Apple's success story

Although there is now a complete range of iPod players available – from the budget flash memory shuffle to the top-end photo – when most people talk about the iPod they are usually referring to the basic hard disk model.

The 20 Gigabyte iPod has become one of the most coveted consumer electronics items and is hugely popular with everyone from music fans through to computer geeks.

Although the iPods have maintained an upright style and that trademark white finish, Apple is actually on to its fourth generation of the player.

iPod First Generation

The first iPod was launched on October 23 2001. Designed by British engineer/stylist Jonathan Ive it featured a five Gigabyte hard disk which Apple claimed would enable its user to store around 1000 songs. What was astonishing about the original iPod wasn't so much its features, which included an 10 hour battery life and a Firewire port which let users transfer songs to the device much faster than they would using USB connectors, but its design. Whereas previous hard disk players had been big and bulky, and in many instances styled to look like personal CD players, the iPod was small, cute and pocketable and weighed just a few ounces.

Critics also praised its small display, a real breakthrough at the time, and highlighted its simple to operate scroll wheel, which gave the user instant access to the tracks stored on the device, as a real innovation. A model capable of storing up to 10 Gigabytes of music followed soon after.

Yet while the world seemed impressed by the quality of the original player, there were some computer owners who felt the original iPod was a real slap in the face. Firstly the original iPod was Mac-only and wouldn't work with Windows PCs. Secondly the player wouldn't work with all Macs, only those with the magical Firewire connection – and owners of the original iMac – had to upgrade their hardware to get the device to work with the player.

Nevertheless Apple had thrown down the gauntlet to the personal audio player manufacturers and had created a product that was truly groundbreaking in terms of its design, functionality and its performance.

iPod Second Generation

On July 17 2002 Apple CEO Steve Jobs delivered the news that music-loving users of Microsoft Windows PCs had been waiting for. He unveiled a new series of iPods, dubbed the second-generation models, which for the first time would work with PCs as well as Macs. Apple had also tweaked the iPod line up too so that in addition to the five Gigabyte model that was originally launched there was also a 10 Gigabyte player that was 10 per cent thinner than

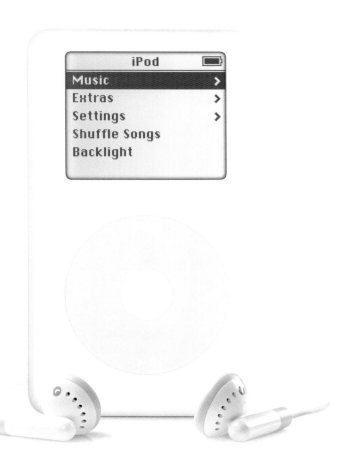

The standard iPod

Apple's main hard disk player

its first generation cousin. But the other big story was the first appearance of a 20 Gigabyte iPod. This went on sale for around $500 and quickly become the most popular Apple music player.

Although it kept the same basic design as the first generation players Apple had made a few adjustments to the iPods, updating the software to support a new iTunes 3 Smart Playlist feature and delivering more browsing features such as organization by composer. Apple also added a clock and a calendar to the iPod, so with time and date facilities – as well as space for holding contacts – the iPod was well on its way to becoming a fully mini PDA.

There was also an adjustment to the player as Apple replaced the mechanical scroll wheel with a touch-sensitive, non-moving one which could detect the motion of the user's finger circling

Needless to say with Apple now offering the iPod to Windows users as well as Mac owners the player went on to become one of the most coveted consumer electronics items of 2002.

There are still second generation iPod for sale on online auction sites like eBay, however, no matter how cheap they are, they aren't worth the

investment largely as the rechargeable batteries often offer a great deal less capacity than the eight hours they held when new, and it is not really prudent to replace the battery.

iPod Third Generation

The third generation iPod, announced on April 28 2003, is arguably the real breakthrough model for Apple and marks the time that the iPod went from being a geeky toy to a must-have gadget for the music lover. The big news was that the iPod was even thinner and lighter than before and arguably more attractive thanks to its curved edges. Over the lifespan of the 3G iPod the player was available in 10, 15, 20, 30 and even 40 Gigabyte storage capacities – the models with larger hard disks were obviously a little bigger.

Apple had also made the new iPod a little simpler to use by adding touch-sensitive buttons to control the menu, forward, pause etc, which were located underneath the display. These buttons were backlit with a red glow, enabling iPod users to operate their players in the dark.

Another big change was the addition of a cradle called the iPod Dock, which either accompanied the player or could be bought separately depending on which model the user bought.

Another minor upgrade was that the new iPod worked with both Windows and Macs. Previously owners of different computer operating systems had to ensure they bought the correct model of iPod to suit their hardware.

At this time the significance of AAC (Advanced Audio Codec) became apparent. Since the first generation, iPods could play both MP3s and AAC files. And in 2003 Apple launched its iTunes online music store in the US.

This enabled users to download legitimately tracks in the high quality AAC format, which they could then port onto their player.

Some iPod users prefer AAC as a format over MP3 for transferring music from their CDs to digital files. AAC generally offers better quality performance than MP3 yet uses slightly smaller file sizes.

So, for example, Apple claimed that users could store roughly 5000 songs encoded in 128-Kbps AAC format on the 20 Gigabyte third generation.

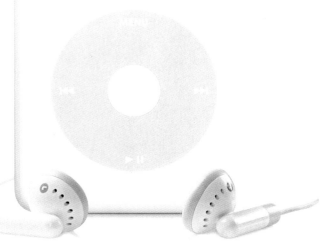

Left:
The iPod plays back MP3 and AAC files as well as other Apple formats such as the innovative Lossless system.

The standard iPod
Today's iPod

iPod Fourth Generation

At the time of writing this is the current iPod currently and will probably remain on sale until at least the middle of 2005.

It was first unveiled in an exclusive interview Apple CEO Steve Jobs gave to Newsweek magazine in July 2004, and went on sale soon afterwards. Once again the new model was slightly smaller and lighter than its predecessor and arguably a little more attractive too.

The big change was that the click wheel for controlling the player that first appeared on the iPod mini was now on the main iPod too. Some critics loved the click wheel, with other Apple diehards arguing it was a step in the wrong direction for Apple and that it actually made the iPod more difficult to use.

There were some other key changes largely concerning the battery. In a response to accusations that the iPod was falling behind the competition in terms of the battery life it offered, the new fourth generation players ran for 12 hours before they needed a recharge rather than their predecessors' eight.

Another slight change was that the player's battery could now be recharged via a USB connection, which meant that those traveling only need take the player and a USB lead with them and not the cradle or mains recharger.

Initially the fourth generation iPod was available in 20 and 40 Gigabyte versions though the 40 Gig was phased out in early 2005 – the iPod photo models with their 30- and 60-Gigabyte capacities taking up the high-end of the iPod range. The 20 Gigabyte iPod currently sells for around $299 (£209 in the UK) – though this may drop in the summer as a response to the launch of the Sony NW-HD5.

In some countries users can also buy the iPod+HP, a HP branded version of the 20 and 40 Gigabyte fourth generation iPods. There are very minor cosmetic differences between the HP and Apple players – the HP iPod even has an Apple logo engraved on the back of the case.

In fact the one advantage the HP model may have over its Apple sibling is that it is often sold at a slightly cheaper price.

There is one other fourth generation iPod that is available - the special edition version of the player that was launched to commemorate the debut of the new U2 album 'How to Dismantle an Atomic Bomb' in 2004.

This 20 Gigabyte player is finished in black and red and comes with a host of U2 tracks already stored on the model.

These are still available via online auction sites like eBay where they sell for around $220.

iPod Fifth Generation

If you want to see what the next generation of iPod will be like you need to try web sites like www.ipod.lounge.com and www.thinksecret.com. Here iPod obsessives have been working away on their Macs to produce images of what they imagine the next generation of iPods might look like.

The standard iPod
The future

At the moment no one knows what the fifth generation of iPods will be like and when they will launch. It's likely, though, when it does arrive that there will be some fairly serious surgery as Apple now faces some stiff competition from the likes of Sony, Creative and Samsung as well as music-playing cellphones.

Apple is sure to improve the battery life, offering around twenty hours from one charge. It is also likely to follow Sony down the removable battery route enabling customers to buy replacement batteries cheaply from the shopping mall or the High Street.

With hard drives shrinking in size Apple may also reduce the size of the player significantly so it is at least on a par with some of its more compact rivals. A color screen seems a certainty along with image and maybe even movie playback.

Of course this is all pure speculation, but with opposition now circling around the iPod Apple needs to upgrade its player quickly to maintain its market lead.

Left:
If you really like the player, you can also buy socks to go with it now.

Fourth generation
iPod basics

Ok, so you have now bought your new 4G iPod.
Here are a few basic tips on how to use it.

Why buy the 4G iPod?

It is arguably the most elegant and superbly
manufactured digital music player available. Other
players may boast facilities that the iPod doesn't have,
but few can match it for simplicity of use for both the
player and its accompanying iTunes software. The
player doesn't only look good – it sounds great too. It
also works with the iTunes online music store, the
most popular of all music download websites. For
Mac owners it really is the only choice, while there are
other players that work with Apple computers, none
function as intuitively and as cleverly as the iPod.
Another reason to buy the 4G iPod is that its 20
Gigabyte hard disk will store around 5000 songs. This
should be more than enough for all but the most
demanding digital music user.

What's in the box?

In addition to those now-ubiquitous white
earbud headphones, the 4G iPod comes with
an AC adapter, FireWire cable and a USB 2.0 cable

What audio formats does the 4G iPod play?

AAC (16 to 320 Kbps), Protected AAC (from iTunes
Music Store), MP3 (16 to 320 Kbps), MP3 VBR, Audible
(formats 2, 3, and 4), Apple Lossless, WAV, AIFF

Transferring songs to the player

This is relatively simple. Simply connect the player
to the PC/Mac using USB 2.0 or Firewire. Open up
iTunes and then drag and drop a song or a playlist
to the player icon in the 'Source' list. If you prefer
you can activate Auto Sync. When you connect
your iPod this works out which new tracks you
have ripped to the computer and then transfers
them automatically.

How do I delete songs on the player?

You simply select the player in the iTunes 'Source'
list, select a song or playlist and then press delete.

How do I recharge the battery?

Depending on which iPod you have you either
recharge the battery by connecting it to its

The standard iPod
How to use your iPod

accompanying recharging cable or place it in its docking cradle. For more recent iPods (the fourth generation models) you can recharge simply by connecting the player to a computer via USB. The battery is around 80 per cent charged in an hour and fully changed after around three hours.

How do I browse for a song?

Click on the main button and then choose 'Browse.' You then find the songs by track, artist or album. When you have found the track you want press the select button.

How do I choose a playlist?

The playlists you set up on iTunes will automatically transfer to the iPod. To find them you just hit the menu button and cycle down to the playlist option.

How do I choose shuffle?

Click the menu button and then choose 'Settings.' In 'Settings' you are given a shuffle option. You can then set the player to randomly play tracks across all songs or a particular album.

How do I replace the iPod's battery?

Apple has its own battery replacement service. See the Apple website for your country for more details.

There are however secondary companies offering DIY replacement kits though we would normally recommend you stay with Apple.

How do I stop the player from auto syncing when I connect it to the computer?

For some users manually transferring tracks, rather than auto syncing, is a much better option especially if they have more music on their computer than they have storage space on their iPod. To switch off auto sync when users first connect the iPod to a computer, then hold down the 'Shift + Ctrl' keys in Windows or 'CMD + Option' keys if they are using as Mac. After around thirty seconds users then need to click on the iPod icon in iTunes' 'Source' column and select 'iPod Options'. Then it is case of ticking the box which says 'manually mange songs and playlists'.

How long will my iPod battery last?

This depends on how much you recharge the battery. The average battery is supposed to last around 500 charges but users know from experience that this is a fairly optimistic assessment. It is also worth ensuring that the battery is fully charged regularly and try not to let the player completely discharge as this impacts on the longevity of the battery. When it gets lower than two bars it is probably worth recharging it.

Can several iPods be connected to the same computer?

Yes, there are a couple of ways of doing this. Firstly users can do this by having separate log in accounts into iTunes. The iTunes will then sync their tracks to their specific accounts. Users can however have the same log in account provided the auto sync feature is switched off.

What if all my music in the WMA (Windows Media Audio) format?

WMA files are not compatible with Apple players so you'll have to convert them to another format. The best way is to re-import all you music as MP3 or AAC files. It is a real pain but is probably best if you intend to stick with Apple players in the future. Alternatively you can use software like dBPowerAMP Music Converter (www.dbpoweramp.com) which will transfer the tracks but you will lose some sound quality. This may be your only option if you don't have the original CDs to hand.

Left:
The Apple iPod syncs brilliantly with the iTunes software making transfer of tracks to the player a real breeze.

iPod Photo

The color screen player

If you're thinking of buying an iPod photo we'll give you some brief background information and then show you how to transfer images from your computer or digital camera, how to view those images and then take you through transferring music files onto your player.

iPod Photo

Benefits of the color screen

During 2003 and 2004 a host of manufacturers started to develop hard disk and flash-memory personal devices that featured screens so they could display image and video files. Having dominated the hard disk based audio market, it was expected that Apple would leap in with an image/video model of its own.

Why the color screen?

However it wasn't until 2004 that the company finally unveiled its first player with a colour screen – the iPod photo. At first glance there isn't much to choose between the iPod photo and the standard 4G iPod.

Both are finished in white, boast the click wheel menu navigation system and are roughly the small size.

The big change is when you switch the screen on; instead of the mono display of the standard 4G iPod the photo version boasts a rich 220x176-pixel resolution, 65,000 color screen.

There are three key reasons why Apple added the color screen. Firstly it threw in color to keep up with rivals like iriver who were already offering color screen players. Secondly the color screen meant that, for the first time, iPod users could view album artwork on the screen of the player. If the artwork had been downloaded via iTunes – all tracks transferred from the iTunes music store come with album artwork – this pops up on the screen when the track/album is playing. It appears as an icon first, which, when the user clicks it delivers artwork that fills up most of the screen. It might sound like a gimmick, but many iPod users have hundreds of

Right:
The iPod photo comes with software that makes it simple to transfer images from your computer to the player.

iPod Photo
Why buy a photo?

Right:
Cosmetically there isn't a great deal to choose between the 4G iPod and the iPod photo apart from the photo's superb color screen

albums on their player and the album artwork provides a good way of navigating through them. Lastly the color screen meant that iPod users could see JPEG photo images on their player's screen. Previous iPods had been able to carry around JPEG files (or anything else that could be stored on the hard drive), but none had the color screen required to display them. The images that the photo displays are really good quality and users can transfer shots to the player in a number of ways (read on for more details).

Even without its image playing ability the iPod photo was a clear leap for Apple. The player was initially available in 40 and 60 Gigabyte (a 30 Gig and a new 60 Gig photo followed in spring 2005) versions boasted a battery life of around 15 hours, significantly more than previous players – double the power of the 3G iPod – and, thanks to its color screen, was arguably the easiest iPod to use.

It is quite likely that color screens will become standard on future iPods and that the name iPod photo will disappear as many Apple players will boast these facilities.

There are however a few issues surrounding the iPod photo, and these are explored elsewhere in this chapter. It ought to be added too that some critics saw the iPod photo as a missed opportunity in that Apple had only chosen to add image compatibility to its players and not video. A video playing iPod is surely a must for Apple, but when it will arrive is anyone's guess.

Why buy an iPod Photo?

For many consumers the big reason to buy the photo is so that they can carry round and display their images on the player as well as listen to their music. For others the photo is worth having as it is the high-end Apple music player with the best battery life, highest amount of storage and easiest to use interface.

How do you get images on to the iPod photo?

There are a number of ways of doing this. The obvious one is to transfer all the images stored on your PC or Mac's hard drive via the photo transfer system in the version of iTunes that accompanies the player. If you have already spent time organizing

your images using iPhoto on a Mac, or either Adobe Album 2.0 or Adobe Photoshop Elements 3.0 on a PC, iTunes will import your collection wholesale. If you have auto-sync activated each time you connect the iPod photo to your computer it will automatically transfer the photo files for you Suppose, though, you are on the go and want to import images directly from your digital camera to the iPod photo? To achieve this Apple offers the $29 iPod Camera Connector. This works by plugging the iPod Camera Connector into the iPod dock and then plugging your camera's USB cable into the other end of the Connector. Your images will then transfer to the iPod. The Connector isn't compatible with all digital cameras – there's full list of cameras the connector works with on the Apple website.

How do you view the images?

There are two different ways of viewing the photos. You can either chose them manually or view them a slide show. To see them manually click on 'Photo Library' and the player will then show thumbnails of 25 images. You move through the images using the click wheel and then when you find the photo you want simply press the action button. You can also organize your photos into – for example – holiday

iPod Photo
How to use the photo

photos in one folder and work shots in another. You can organize your images this way using the iTunes software. Another neat touch is the 'Last 12 Months' option which brings up the images you have snapped in the last year The slideshow mode presents the images in your collection in a number of different ways. You can chose to have them in order or randomized, displayed within 2, 3, 5, 10, 20, or unlimited seconds of delay, or shown with or without musical accompaniment.

What size are the images?
The image takes up pretty much all of the iPod photo's screen if they are shot in landscape mode. If they were shot in portrait mode there are black bars at the sides.

Can I view those images anywhere else?
One of the best features of the iPod photo is that it can output the images on the player to a TV screen creating a true slideshow. Run an S-Video cable from the photo to the TV and you can view images on the big screen. You can also choose whether you want the images shown in widescreen or 4:3 formats. Another bonus is that you can choose any of the music on your iPod to accompany the slideshow. This is relayed via your TV or through an external sound system.

Which photo formats is the iPod photo compatible with?
The file formats varies a little between Mac and PC. On the Mac, the photo's accompanying iTunes 4.7 software can recognize these file formats from your iPhoto Library: JPG, TIFF, PICT, GIF, PNG, JPG2000 or JP2, PSD, SGI, and BMP On Windows, iTunes 4.7 can recognize these file formats from Adobe PhotoShop Album and Adobe PhotoShop Elements: JPG, JPEG, BMP, GIF, TIF, TIFF, and PNG .

What's in the box?
There's a belt-clipped carrying case, a soft carry bag, USB and FireWire data cables, white earbuds, and a power supply. Most importantly the iPod photo comes with the iPod photo Dock, which is the same as Apple's Audio Dock in that it sports a line-out audio port and a dock connector port but also contains an S-Video output for connecting to your TV. Annoyingly there's no S-Video cable include so if you haven't got one you'll have to buy one for yourself.

What audio formats does the iPod photo play?
AAC (16 to 320 Kbps), Protected AAC (from iTunes Music Store), MP3 (16 to 320 Kbps), MP3 VBR, Audible (formats 2, 3, and 4), Apple Lossless, WAV, AIFF

Transferring songs to the player

The iPod photo works in similar way to the main 20 Gigabyte iPod player. Simply connect the player to the PC/Mac using USB 2.0 or Firewire. Open up iTunes and then drag and drop a song or a playlist to the player icon in the 'Source' list. If you prefer you can activate Auto Sync. When you connect your iPod this works out which new tracks you have ripped to the computer and then transfers them automatically.

How do I delete songs on the player?

You simply select the player in the iTunes 'Source' list, select a song or playlist and then press delete.

How do I recharge the battery?

The photo can be recharged either using an adapter or by connecting the player to a computer via USB. The battery is around 80 per cent charged in an hour and fully changed after around three hours.

How do I browse for a song?

Click on the main button and then choose 'Browse.' You then find the songs by track, artist or album. When you have found the track you want press the select button.

How do I choose a playlist?

The playlists you set up on iTunes will automatically transfer to the photo. To find them you just hit the menu button and cycle down to the playlist option.

How do I choose shuffle?

Click the menu button and then choose 'Settings.' In 'Settings' you are given a shuffle option. You can then set the player to randomly play tracks across all songs or a particular album.

How do I replace the iPod's battery?

Apple has its own battery replacement service. See the Apple website for your country for more details. There are however secondary companies offering DIY replacement kits though we would normally recommend you stay with Apple.

For details on how to use the iPod photo see the answers to the questions posed in the chapter 7.

iPod Mini

Apple's stylish player

The iPod mini has become a real fashion accessory. We'll explain what's in it for you, the range of colors and then show you how to start transferring your music on to it.

iPod Mini

Apple's most stylish player

Between 2001 and 2004 Apple brought out a series of iPods, all of which were roughly the same size and shape and sported the player's trademark white finish. Then in early 2004 the company rewrote the rule book by introducing a sibling model to the iPod – the iPod mini.

Significantly smaller than the existing standard Apple players the mini was also cheaper and had fewer features. It also featured a five Gigabyte hard disk drive as opposed to the 20 Gigabyte drives of the existing iPod), which Apple claimed was enough to store around 1250 tunes. However, in true Apple style, the mini featured a wonderfully alluring design and came in five different colors from shiny silver to aquamarine blue. It also boasted an innovation for the iPod in the click wheel which has subsequently been adopted across much of the iPod family.

Fashion accessory

When the iPod mini was finally launched in spring 2004 both online and traditional retailers reported a massive wave of sales. In New York it was rumored that some well heeled young women were even buying three or four different-colored minis to match their many outfits. Such was its popularity, that the global launch of the iPod mini was delayed several months, and even when countries like the UK did receive their first minis demand completely outstripped the limited supply.

The iPod mini went on to be a huge success, so much so that in 2005 Apple took the wraps off a second generation of the player. The new model was available with either four or six Gigabyte hard disks yet was roughly the same size as its predecessor. Apple had also significantly improved the iPod mini's battery performance with the new player delivering eighteen hours of playing time as

Previous page:
The iPod mini has less storage than the standard iPod and the iPod photo. Yet for many users its four Gigabyte hard disk (which can store around 1000 songs) is more than enough.

Right:
The iPod mini now comes in four different colors. Originally it was available in five, but when the 2nd generation player was launched Apple decided that the gold version was surplus to requirements.

opposed to the rather poor eight hours of its first incarnation. Cosmetically the second generation player was very similar to its predecessor as Apple kept both the scroll wheel and the screen. However there was good news for consumers in that Apple dropped the price of the player with the four Gigabyte model retailing for $199 while the six gig version sold for $249.

The mini is also one of Apple's toughest players in that its matte anodized aluminum case resists stains and scratches. It has also spawned a small industry of companies who produce all manner of cases for the player. One favorite is the C Ronson Hoodie, a toweling based jacket for the mini that has its own hood.

Why buy the iPod mini?

When it was first launched the iPod mini was largely targeted at women and billed as a fashion accessory as much as a music player. The mini has now established itself though, and is apparently bought in roughly equal numbers by men and women. Essentially the mini is a cut down version of the standard iPod. It may have less storage than the full iPod, but even the four Gigabyte version which has room, Apple claims, for over 1000 tunes (the six Gigabyte apparently houses 1500 tunes) is probably more than enough for all but the most dedicated digital music lovers. The cut down price also gives users a chance to own an iPod without having to pay a huge amount more than they would for a quality personal CD player.

iPod Mini
Using the mini

One thing that isn't cut down is the battery life. Bearing in mind that the current 20 Gigabyte iPod has a battery life of just twelve hours the eighteen hours offered by the mini is very impressive indeed. There are some critics who say that the iPod's white finish now looks rather dated. So in some ways the iPod mini, with its four bold colour finishes, provided a breath of fresh air. Its cute, upright styling and small pocketable size also make it a very attractive proposition. Basically if you are thinking about buying an iPod and can't ever imagine having hundreds of albums on your player the mini is the Apple model to buy. Its budget price and small size are bonuses.

What's in the box?
In addition to its white earbud headphones the iPod mini comes with a belt clip and a USB 2.0 cable.

What audio formats does the iPod mini play?
AAC (16 to 320 Kbps), Protected AAC (from iTunes Music Store), MP3 (16 to 320 Kbps), MP3 VBR, Audible (formats 2, 3, and 4), Apple Lossless, WAV, AIFF

What colours is the iPod mini available in?
The original version of the mini, which had a five Gigabyte hard disk, shipped in five colors; silver, blue, green, gold and pink. The second generation version was available in just four colors Apple having decided that the gold version was surplus to requirements.

Transferring songs to the player
The iPod mini works in a similar way to the standard iPod. Simply connect the player to the PC/Mac using USB 2.0. Open up iTunes and then drag and drop a song or a playlist to the player icon in the 'Source' list. If you prefer you can activate Auto Sync. When you connect your iPod this works out which new tracks you have ripped to the computer and then transfers them automatically.

How do I delete songs on the player?
You simply select the player in the iTunes 'Source' list, select a song or playlist and then press delete.

How do I recharge the battery?
Unlike some other iPods the mini doesn't come with an AC adapter – you pay extra for that. So to charge the player you have to connect it to the USB 2.0 port on your PC/Mac. The battery is around 80 per cent charged in an hour and fully changed after around three hours.

How do I browse for a song?
Click on the main button and then choose 'Browse.' You then find the songs by track, artist or album. When you have found the track you want press the select button.

How do I choose a playlist?
The playlists you set up on iTunes will automatically transfer to the iPod mini. To find them you just hit the menu button and cycle down to the playlist option.

How do I choose shuffle?
Click the menu button and then choose 'Settings.' In 'Settings' you are given a shuffle option. You can then set the player to randomly play tracks across all songs or a particular album.

How do I replace the iPod mini's battery?
Apple has its own battery replacement service. See the Apple website for your country's details.

Below:
The iPod mini works with the iTunes software in a very similar way to the standard 4G iPod, so transferring tracks to and from the player to a computer like this Mac mini is very simple.

iPod Shuffle

Apple's flash player

In this chapter we introduce you to the iPod shuffle, run through transferring songs and recharging the battery and examine its merits and drawbacks.

iPod Shuffle
Apple's flash player

Flash memory-based digital music players have been around for quite some time now, with companies like Creative and Sony already on their fifth and sixth generation models. So it was something of a surprise in early 2005 when Apple took the wraps off its debut flash based player – the iPod shuffle.

The cheapest and simplest to use of all the iPods, the shuffle also breaks with many of the key iPod traditions in that it doesn't feature a scroll wheel, won't play back Apple's proprietary high quality music formats and, most important of all, doesn't include a screen.

The shuffle is designed for those on the move – it is ideal for joggers as its flash memory can withstand the odd bump or two – or users who want a small player but don't want the bulk of an iPod or an iPod mini. It is also aimed at those who like surprises, for – and the clue is in its name – the shuffle mainly plays tracks randomly. When connected to a PC or Mac it takes a series of tracks from the computer randomly – though apparently it does tend to favor most played tunes – and

transfers them onto the flash memory. These are then mixed up and played back randomly

Users can however play tracks in a certain order or choose which tracks to fill the shuffle with. However their control over the choice of what they listen to, when playing their selections back, is limited as the shuffle has no screen.

It might be inexpensive with the 512 MB (120 tunes) version retailing for $99 (£69 in the UK) and the one gigabyte (240 tunes) version selling for $149 (£99 in the UK) but the shuffle bears all the key Apple/iPod trademarks.

It sports its traditional white plastic finish, plays back both MP3 and AAC music files and is compatible with music downloaded via the iTunes music store.

Since its launch the iPod shuffle has been a huge success with a recent report claiming that it has now taken around 60 per cent of the flash memory-based digital music player market.

It is clear that for many buyers its styling, simplicity of use, and price have more than compensated for its lack of facilities.

Why buy the iPod shuffle?

With the iPod shuffle Apple is targeting two different types of buyers; diehard iPod owners who fancy a second small, take anywhere player and iPod newbies attracted by the player's size and budget price.

For the diehards the shuffle is an obvious purchase. It works well with iTunes and provides a fun way of delivering a few tunes for those times when carrying round a full size iPod would be inappropriate.

For the newbies the appeal of the shuffle is that it is not just cheap, it is also Apple's easiest to use player. The tracks load instantaneously from the iTunes software on a PC or Mac and then all users have to

Left:
It took a long while for Apple to enter the flash memory based player market – but when it did its model, the iPod shuffle, proved to be yet another huge success.

iPod Shuffle
Why buy the shuffle?

do to control the device is operate the play, pause, stop, last track and next track buttons. If you want to sample an iPod player but don't want to pay a great deal of cash for it the shuffle is a very easy way in. It should be added though that there are many other better specified flash memory players which sell for roughly around the same price as the shuffle. So if you want a model with a screen, FM radio tuner and voice recording facilities and aren't too bothered about compatibility with the iTunes music store then shop around.

What's in the box?
There's no AC adapter for recharging or even a USB connection. That's because the shuffle has a USB socket built it. The player does however come with the trademark Apple white earbud headphones, a lanyard so that you wear the shuffle round your neck and also a USB cap

What audio formats does the iPod shufffle play?
The shuffle plays almost all the major music formats including; MP3 (8 to 320 Kbps), MP3 VBR, AAC (8 to 320 Kbps), Protected AAC (from iTunes Music Store, M4A, M4B, M4P), Audible (formats 2, 3, and 4) and

WAV. It won't however play back high quality formats like Apple Lossless and AIFF.

Transferring songs to the player
You can transfer songs to the player into two ways. The easy way is to let it auto sync with your collection. Once connected you choose the 'Auto Fill' button and the shuffle randomly selects music from iTunes, though it does have a slight bias towards your most played tracks, which it then adds to the player's flash memory. If you want to put specific tracks or a playlist on to the shuffle you transfer it in the usual way which involves dragging and dropping a playlist/track on to the shuffle icon in iTunes.

How do I recharge the battery?
The only way to recharge the battery is to connect the shuffle to a PC or Mac via its integrated USB 2.0 connector. The battery is around 80 per cent charged in an hour and fully changed after around three hours.

How do I browse for a song?
The shuffle has very limited controls. There's no menu system and scroll wheel which are the staples of other iPods. Instead users only have four small

buttons with a larger white play/pause button in the center. On the back is an on/off switch. As there's no screen there is no way of knowing which track is playing.

How long does the iPod shuffle battery last?

Apple says that the shuffle battery will last for around twelve hours before it needs a recharge. However many users claims that this figure is a little on the low side and they actually got more like fifteen hours of playback. This is still relatively low compared to some flash based players which have battery life of thirty hours or more.

Will Apple make more flash memory based players?

Well no one knows for sure, but it is very likely that it will. The clever money is on a deluxe flash player complete with a screen and improved battery life to take on rival Sony Walkmans. Some websites are even predicting a kind of iPod mini/shuffle hybrid that has many of the mini's features but uses flash memory rather than a hard disk.

Left:
The shuffle is available with two storage capacities – 512MB or one Gigabyte.

iPod accessories

The basics

Now you have your iPod it is time to accessorize. There is a wide range of iPod add-ons from cases and bags through to headphones & Speakers

iPod accessories
The basics

Apple excels at creating portable players that have become icons of their era, with design and functionality going hand in hand with street credibility and fashion, but the company has also understood the importance of accessories. Whether it's a highly useful add-on that provides advanced functionality, or a gadget that provides a bit more branded cool to the customers, Apple has got a product to suit pretty much every need.

iPod Store

Apple makes a number of accessories and add-ons itself, but it's not averse to sharing the burden with other companies as well, and you'll find a number of non-Apple branded iPod accessories available for purchase on the official Apple online Store with prices that can vary in their affordability.

It's always worth checking the Apple store out first before looking elsewhere, because often – though not always – the company already sells the best value for money option.

You can also read the feedback supplied by earlier customers who have reviewed their purchases, allowing you to browse the selection of products to find the best one for you.

One downside is that the company doesn't always provide a huge amount of detail about the products for sale, so if you're intending on making a big purchase you should think about checking the manufacturer's site first to make sure you've got all the details and specifications.

Right:
There is now a large range of iPod accessories including all kinds of cases and even Apple iPod socks

Armbands

Wearing your music player round your arm may have seemed like a strange idea a few years ago, but more and more people have embraced the concept, and you'll now find a wide selection of official and unofficial bands to choose from. They're great for runners and people already over-burdened with bags who want to be able to get hold of the controls without having to rummage through purses or bags to find their players. The one downside is, of course that they can make you into a prime target for thieves, and it's worth considering where you're intending to wear the player before you strap it to your arm for the day.

The iPod mini armbands come in a selection of colors designed to match or contrast with your player. Currently, gray, blue, orange, pink and yellow are available. These basic bands are made from stretchable materials with a Velcro fastening and a plastic holder that the player clips securely into. They currently cost around $29.

For a more advanced option for your iPod mini, Apple also sells the XtremeMac SportWrap iPod Mini Armband ($29.95). This, as the name suggests, is designed for more extreme sporting uses, offering

iPod accessories
The basics

a water-resistant, Neoprene casing that protects your mini from the weather when you're jogging or cycling. The player can be controlled through the clear plastic front of the armband and the headphone jack is self-sealing to keep moisture away, so you don't need to expose it to the weather in order to operate it. There's also an earbud holder that lets you store your earphones, or just the excess cord, out of the way when you're on the move.

Also for sporty types is the $34.95 Marware SportSuite Convertible, a case that provides rugged protection with water resistant hard neoprene outer case, a lined interior and plastic impact protectors that should help it to survive regular knocks and jolts. The hard lid can be flipped open to reveal the player inside, and you can operate the controls from here. The SportSuite comes with a belt clip attachment or an arm band, so you can wear it wherever you choose, and the headphone and remote pocket on the lid let you keep everything safe and secure together.

An alternative to the armband selection for your iPod mini is the $24.95 Incase Music Belt, a neoprene case that you can strap round your waist. It come with a selection of pockets and pouches for your player, as well as room for earbuds, keys, cards, and anything

else you need to stow. The selection for standard iPods is not quite as wide, but the XtremeMac SportWrap Armband, Marware SportSuite Convertible and Incase Music Belt are all available to fit at the same prices as the iPod mini versions.

The iPod photo is slightly too large to make wearing it round your arm a feasible option, whereas the small iPod shuffle has been designed from day one as a player that's ideal for strapping to your body, with an Apple-branded armband available as well as an XtremeMac SportWrap.

Cases

Cases are a popular addition to iPods and although the players have been built to be relatively sturdy, they could always benefit from a bit of extra protection, even if it's only to keep them scratch free as they travel around in your bag.

The shuffle has a Sport Case ($29) that Apple produces, offering bump protection and a neckstrap design so you can where it like a pendant necklace, and all the other players have the standard black nylon cases with belt clips. But there are more adventurous cases on offer, including the colorful,

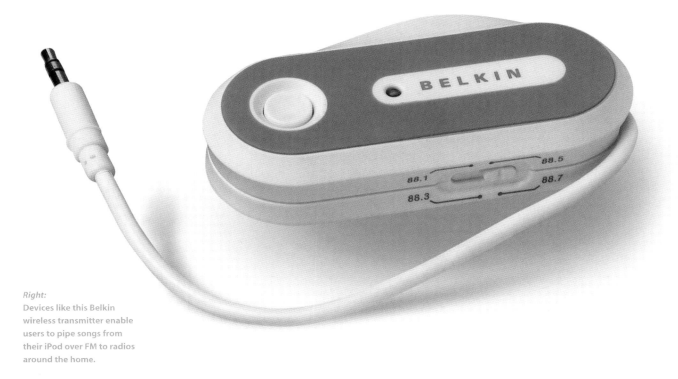

Right:
Devices like this Belkin
wireless transmitter enable
users to pipe songs from
their iPod over FM to radios
around the home.

iPod accessories
The basics

knitted iPod Socks ($29) from Apple that offer a fun alternative to many of the more staid, leather products available.

But if staid leather what you're after, you'll find that in plentiful supply as well, with companies such as XtremeMac will be happy to provide you with one, while Timbuk2, Monster and Incase supply neoprene and other hardwearing alternatives to leather.

Many of these offer extra pockets and pouches for storing all sorts of extra cables as well as the earbuds, making them great for people wanting to stay fully equipped wherever they happen to be.

Belkin, meanwhile, has taken the colorful nature of the iPod minis to heart and come up with some complementary cases in leather, providing enough protection for travel in a purse or bag.

And if it's color that appeals to you, you may want to look at the selection of "skins". These are slightly different to normal cases because, as the name suggest, they are designed to act as second skins to the players, providing protection from knocks and scrapes, without adding extra bulk. Speck, XtremeMac and iSkin are the main manufacturers that offer their products on the Apple store, with a vast array of colors available that let you add a bit

of a personal touch to the white players – and keep the minis looking cheerful. There's even a bright green Wasabi skin from iSkin that glows green in the dark.

Docks and Cables

Although the iPod range has been designed to plug into your computer's FireWire or USB port without any trouble, it's nice to have the option of a dock that lets you charge and synchronize your player without having to worry about plugging in cables every time.

All of the players have an Apple-branded dock attached, with all of them costing $39 apart from the shuffle dock, which costs $29. The iPod shuffle dock only connects via USB 2.0 but for the other players you can buy the cables to charge and connect the docks via either USB 2.0 or FireWire.

These all include an audio line out connector as well, which means you can hook your player up to the stereo to play music through its speakers.

The iPod photo dock also comes with an S-Video

connector so you can plug it straight into a TV or compatible computer to play slideshows of your photos. Alternatively, you can purchase the $19 AV Cable that will provide a composite video and audio output from your iPod photo's headphone, or the dock's line out socket.

Seventy-nine dollars will buy you an iPod Stereo Connector Kit which contains everything you need to connect your iPod or iPod mini (not photo or shuffle) to a home stereo system. For this you get the iPod Dock, power adapter, dock connector to FireWire cable and a Monster Cable Mini-Stereo to RCA Cable, which connects your dock to the audio input on your home stereo receiver.

Monster also makes a number of other cable products for iPods, including the iCable for iPod Stereo 7ft for $29.95. This apparently provides excellent quality connection from your iPod to your sound system.

There's also the Monster iTV Link for iPod photo and Powerbook so you can play your photo slideshows on your television or Powerbook.

There's also a selection of splitters that plug into your headphone jack so that two people can listen at once.

Left:
Griffin's iTrip FM radio transmitter has become one of the most popular of all iPod add-ons.

iPod accessories
The basics

Left:
Belkin's iPod Media Readers enable users to transfer files directly from storage cards to their iPod.

In-car iPod

If you want to listen to your iPod in the car, you can opt for one of the car cassette adapters from Sony or XtremeMac. These just fit into your cassette deck on you car stereo and plug into your iPod's headset socket, playing tunes through the car speakers.

Alternatively, you can go for one of the FM transmitters from the likes of Griffin, Monster and Belkin which transmits your tunes to your car stereo using FM radio signals. Belkin also does a selection of in-car holders and chargers, allowing you to keep your player powered via the cigarette lighter socket in your vehicle. These gadgets come in a wide selection of styles and prices, starting at just under $20 and going all the way up to nearly $80. It should be noted though that they are in fact illegal to use in the UK and several other European countries.

Add-ons

One of the best thing about portable memory storage devices is their flexibility, and the iPod range is no different: you can get countless types of add-ons and plug ins for your player, which provide

Headphones

a host of new features and functions. Take the Apple iPod Camera Connector ($29), for instance. This plugs into your iPod photo dock connector so that you can then transfer images directly from your camera to your iPod via the mini USB connection on your camera. Or, for more advanced functionality, you can go for the Belkin iPod Media Reader ($70) which adds a card reader to your iPod so you can plug in 6 different types of memory cards, including SD, CF, MMC and Memory Stick.

The Griffin iTalk ($40) turns your iPod into a voice recorder, adding an internal microphone, a microphone socket and also a speaker for playing songs back. And if you like to have your iPod plugged into your sound system at home, you might want to consider a Ten Technology naviPro eX Wireless Remote so you can change tracks and control your player from afar.

Ten Technology also makes more wireless add-ons, such as the naviPlay Bluetooth Stereo Kit. The adapter plugs into your iPod's dock connector, adding Bluetooth wireless connectivity, and the remote plugs into your earbuds, allowing you to control the iPod without having to keep it near you at all times.

Plugging in add-ons means you can get your iPod to do pretty much anything you want it to. But it's the music that's the main focus of the players. The white earbuds that come supplied with your iPod have become pretty iconic in themselves, signaling to everyone that you're wearing a coveted iPod. That doesn't mean you can't try out other earphones though, and the Apple Store has plenty to choose from.

Apple itself makes some in-ear headphones as well as a set that includes a wired remote control so you don't need to get your player out of its bag. Etymotic's ER-6i are also in-ear headphones, but these are designed to go right down into your ear, feeding the sounds directly to your ear canal. They're white in keeping with the standard earphones, and other companies that offer white headphones include Shure with its E5C Sound Isolating Earphones and Altec Lansing's Oyoyo Headphones which come with an over-head band.

Despite being a major competitor, Sony has a number of headphones on offer, including a couple of pairs from its Fontopia Headphone range – one standard, one noise canceling – and a set of high

iPod accessories
The basics

end Sony Studio Monitor MDR-V700DJ Headphones that wouldn't look out of place on a DJ. Another company known for its high quality audio products is Bose and it has a selection of large headphones, including the top of the range Bose QuietComfort 2 Acoustic Noise Canceling Headphones, which at just under $300, are the most expensive in the Apple Store.

JVC also offers a small range of headphones, while Bang & Olufsen sticks with its usual "less is more" policy, offering just one pair of highly stylized, high quality A8 Headphones which go in the ear and also include an over-ear loop.

Nike joins the fray with a selection of rather more affordable headphones, all designed to be lightweight and suitable for sporting enthusiasts. The styles include ear buds with ear hooks, behind the head headphones, and behind the head ear buds, so whichever pair you opt for they should be secure.

They're also all sweat resistant so you don't have to worry about damaging them during a workout.

Speakers

Apple's iPods may have been designed as portable, personal players, but once you've loaded a lifetime of music onto yours you may find yourself wishing you could share the songs with friends, or listen in your living room. Luckily, there's a vast array of speaker sets available that offer varying degrees of portability, power and sound quality.

Sony's SRS-P11Q rounded white personal speakers start the selection off, offering basic plug in passive speakers that don't use an amp and simply plug in instead of your normal earphones. These will set you back around $25. At the top end of the spectrum are Logitech with its Z-5500 5.1 THX Speaker System for nearly $350. This is a 500-watt 5.1 surround system so it's designed for someone looking for something fairly serious to plug an iPod into. With a subwoofer, digital equalizer and a central control unit for changing your sound and level settings, as well as a wireless remote so you can use it like any other sound system.

Bose is also in the high range with speaker sets that cost nearly $300. The Bose SoundDock Digital Music System supports all the iPods that come with a dock connector, but shuffle owners will need to look elsewhere and iPod photo owners will need to purchase an extra cable. This set up provides a charging dock for your iPod as well as a sleek speaker that doesn't look out of place with the iPod design. There's also an infrared remote so you can treat it just like any other stereo system.

If you're looking for something a bit unusual, JBL's range offer some very distinctive designs that will certainly get you noticed. The prices tend to be in the mid range. The JBL Creature II set, for example, is a 3 piece speaker system that includes two desktop speakers and a subwoofer. It will cost you just under $100.

It also marks itself out from the crowd with an unusual undulating design that's more space age than the rest. There are also the curved JBL Duet 2.0 Speakers, which have been designed for either a computer or your music player, and the JBL On Stage speaker which has been

created especially for iPods so you can synchronize and charge it as you play.

Altec Lansing has come up with a speaker set designed especially for iPod mini players. The inMotion Portable Speakers are tiny, battery operated speakers that comes with an amplifier and four micro drivers to help bump up the sound. They can be folded away to make smaller cargo and will charge and synch your mini while playing.

Below
In addition to products specifically for the iPod Apple also sells items like the Airport Extreme which enables its owners to create a wireless network in their home and listen to iTunes music in other rooms.

AirPort Extreme

iPod accessories

The fun stuff

There are many cool iPod accessories out there, bizarre cases and skins, jewelry, speakers and recharging systems, not to mention ways to waterproof and customise your iPod.

iPod accessories
The fun stuff

If you think there's an impressive choice of accessories for your iPod available on the Apple online store, just wait to you start looking at what else is out there. Since Apple started selling its players the number of companies that have sprung up to take advantage of the popularity of the players is phenomenal, with many of them relying almost entirely on the continuation of the iPod for its success.

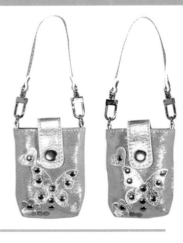

Many of these companies, as we saw in Chapter 11, receive a partial endorsement from Apple, which offers the products for sale in its worldwide stores and online. However, there are many more out there trading entirely unofficially, often selling very specialized products for particular players. And although these offer unofficial merchandize, many of the companies offer some nice, high quality and innovative products that are likely to appeal to iPod customers.

Obviously, because these products aren't endorsed by Apple and since some of them are such small cottage industries, there's no vouching for the quality of the products or the service you'll receive. That's not to say that these sorts of unofficial accessories are in any way underhand or untrustworthy and, in fact, the majority of the unofficial products available are from well-established and well-known companies.

You'll find a lot of items readily available for you to check out in stores before you make a purchase. Even online you'll be covered by certain guarantees and rights as a customer. Don't be afraid to get in touch with the people you're thinking of buying products from and entering into a dialogue with them for reassurance, and to satisfy whatever

Previous page:
The Deco Dock is a rather stylish recharger/speaker system for the iPod shuffle.

Above:
There is now a huge range of cases for the iPod with even some big fashions names like Paul Smith and Gucci offering their own bags.

questions you may have. With so many innovative and appealing products out there, it would be a shame to limit yourself just to Apple's own brand goods – just make sure you check out companies and products before committing to a purchase.

Cases & Skins

Probably the most packed market for iPod accessories is the case and skin market. There are more companies selling cases out there than pretty much anything else, with many of them running small operations out of their own homes as a sideline in their spare time. The largest companies, like Covertec or Slappa also make covers for other electrical gear such as PDAs or other players. And then there are the designer brands that have started getting in on the act, including Paul Smith, Gucci and Burberry, all of which have developed cases for the iPod.

If your budget can't stretch to the $200 and more that is usually charged for the designer cases it doesn't mean you'll have to go without the more unusual cases. There are plenty of companies offering something that's a bit different to the norm. If you're looking for something specific you're pretty

much guaranteed to find it out there somewhere, either from one of the large retailers, or from someone selling their wares on eBay. Spanish company Piel Frama (www.pielframa.com) for example does a range of leather cases for all sorts of gadgets, including all the variants of iPod (apart from shuffles).

They use more unusual leathers, including ostrich and crocodile, so you're sure to have a case that's a bit out of the ordinary. Paag Pak (www.paagpak.com) is one of the many companies that creates fabric pouches that you can slip your iPod into. There's a variety on offer, including fluffy, plastic and embroidered slip cases, as well as the

Below:
There is now even jewelry for the iPod shuffle.

iPod accessories
The fun stuff

company's signature quilted version. But while these may be pretty unique, you'll soon find that there are even more wacky and unusual options for storing your player. A selection of metallic iPod mini cases in blue, yellow or pink are available from Rafe – a company that usually specializes in shoe design. Even more extreme, meanwhile, is the C.Ronson iPod Hoodie – a cover that's designed to look like a miniature hooded top from New York-based designer Charlotte Ronson. Alternatively, the Chuckles (www.chucklescentral.com) crocheted iPod Cozies are designed to resemble animals and, believe it or not, Chuckles is just one of the many companies making woolen cases in cute designs.

For more serious protection, Proporta makes hard, aluminum cases for all but the shuffle that are padded and durable while still providing enough gaps in the Armour for you to control your player. Aluminum cases for shuffles are harder to come by, but Griffin Technology has the iVault, an aluminum hard case for the tiny player.

Alternatively, Proporta also makes a "Crystal" range of clear, toughened, shatter-proof polycarbonate plastic which are available for the shuffle as well as all the other iPods. Proporta, along with Covertec also make durable and very professional, classic

looking leather cases that flip open from the bottom to reveal the player inside. AcmeMade has something similar for the iPod mini and iPod in different colored leather designs, but these open like a book and contain enough space for your headphones.

Waterproofing your iPod may seem like a pretty extreme requirement, but there are some shops out there offering products that should protect your player against the elements. Otterbox (www.otterbox.com) makes a selection of tough, waterproof cases that, when combined with waterproof earphones, can be taken swimming or kayaking. It's also dust proof, sand proof and drop proof, making it a pretty rugged storage house for your player. H2O Audio (www.h2oaudio.com), meanwhile, has a waterproof case for swimmers and shallow diving that also includes a set of waterproof earphones. Currently the company only has products for 3rd and 4th Generation iPods and the iPod mini.

The iPod shuffle seems to be one of the most popular targets for unusual cases. It may be one of the newest players in the iPod camp, but the small flash device already boasts a huge selection of cases, skins and covers. Small companies such as

Wrappers (www.wrappers.typepad.com) offer handmade, embroidered cases that allow you to personalize the player to suit your tastes. And because it is a small company, only a few of each are made, ensuring that you get something that really is a limited edition. DLO Direct (www.dlodirect.com) makes a selection of colored caps that you can pop onto the top of your shuffle to make a more colorful lanyard neck strap holder.

And if you decide that the white of the players just isn't lively enough of your liking you can opt for some colorful skins from companies such as Boxwave (www.boxwave.com) and iSkins (www.iskins.co.uk) that will make your white players a bit brighter and give iPod minis a new look that's both protective and temporary. These allow you to control your iPod and gain access to all the relevant wheels and connectors whilst still protecting the player.

Customization and Modification

Having a design alteration that's temporary is quite an important factor for many users – you may not want to do something you'll regret in the future and can't change. Rubber-style Skins aren't the only solution, however. You can also give stick on patterns and designs a try, and many of them are entirely removable, allowing you to replace ones that have become scuffed and old, or change the colors to suit your mood. Decal Girl (www.decalgirl.com) makes a range of vinyl skins for all the iPod players that are self adhesive. The company promises that these covers can be repositioned and reused and they should come off

Below:
Or if you prefer kitsch this case is obviously inspired by a character from the Star Wars movies.

iPod accessories
The fun stuff

without leaving any sticky residues behind. Also, the company guarantees that the skins won't fade, smudge or discolor. There are plenty of other stores offering similar products, and some of them even allow you to suggest patterns you'd like, or design your own

Cases and covers provide a degree of customization and personalization, especially the limited edition covers from the smaller companies. But if you want to go a step further in altering the appearance of your player, there are plenty of services out there. Turning your player into an item of jeweler seems to be a popular option, with a company such as iPod Jewelry (www.ipodjewelry.com) providing a beaded mesh creation that you can slip over your shuffle to make it look more like a necklace pendant than an iPod.

Jewelry is the main focus for companies such as NYC Peach (www.nycpeach.com), a customization service that will take your iPod and turn it into a sparkling creation using colored lead Swarovski crystals that are bonded one at a time to your player of choice. This is a permanent alteration, so don't go for it unless you're sure you won't change your mind. The service is fairly expensive, but since NYC Peach has made a name for it modifying

celebrities' phones and music players, it's hardly surprising. Crystal Mini (www.crystalmini.com) offers a similar service, but this time you get the iPod (minis only) along with your order. The company also has stores in New York and Paris. Again, this is a fairly expensive service and, if you're feeling creative, you could always opt to lay the crystals yourself. Bling Ring (www.myblingring.com) is one company offering packs of Swarovski stones that you can stick on yourself. And if jewelry isn't your thing, you can always go for clothing. Podbrix (www.podbrix.com) is a very innovative retailer offering t-shirts that come with a shuffle holder. Clip your shuffle into place using the strong, magnetic clasp and the player looks as though it's being held by the silhouette lego-esque character on your shirt.

Speakers

There may be a plentiful supply of speaker sets available from the official iPod store, but that hasn't stopped other companies coming up with their own variations, many of which are ever more innovative and striking. PodGear is a company with a generous selection, including the ShuffleStation, a charging dock and speaker set up for your shuffle.

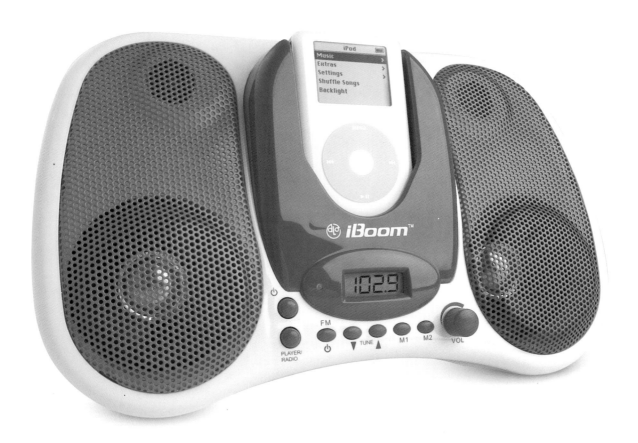

iPod accessories
The fun stuff

The stereo speakers fold away flat when they're not in use and can be powered by battery or by an AC adapter plugged into the wall. The slight catch is that the shuffle's connector is located at the top of the player, so the player has to be turned upside down before it can be plugged into the speakers. Not a problem if you just want to play your tunes out loud, but it makes changing tracks and altering the volume an interesting experience.

Alternatively, you can go for the PocketParty Shuffle, which uses a different design that's even more compact and portable. This time the speakers have a connector on the top, and once the shuffle has been slid into place, the whole unit looks like it belongs together, with the player sitting flush with the rest of the speakers.

A similarly titled, but altogether different product from PodGear is the PocketParty, which has been designed for all the other iPod players apart from the shuffle. This is one of the smallest and most portable speaker sets out there for Apple's jukeboxes, plugging into the top of the iPod, iPod photo and iPod mini and producing sound through the speakers on either end. At the other end of the scale, the iBoom from DLO Direct (www.dlodirect.com) turns your iPod into an old school boom box that

you can carry round on one shoulder. It comes with all the controls on the front panel, enough space for a standard iPod or an iPod mini, an LCD panel that displays the time, and an FM radio.

For something that's entirely unique, visit online store Dr Bott. It's selling a line of bags called the Felicidade Groove Bags. These white bags come complete with a pocket to slide your iPod into and a set of speakers that are built into the front. Connect up your player and you can listen to music pumping out of your bag.

Unusual Extras

When it comes to the iPod it's amazing how many companies have let their imaginations wander, producing all manner of innovative and unusual products, add-ons and accessories.

Many items, such as the DecoDock from Pressure Drop (www.pdrop.com) are all about good design and desirability. The art deco-inspired dock for iPod shuffles doesn't add extra functionality, but with two columns that light up with LEDs on either side of your player, you'll have a little art deco building right there on your desktop.

Other products combine innovation with a design that's obviously meant to reflect the Apple aesthetic. The Solio (www.solio.com) is a portable solar panel that can be used with many different types of player, PDA or phone, but the white styling and curved casing is clearly inspired by the iPod design. This solar powered charger can apparently charge your player while you're out and about, harnessing the sun's energy to bump up the battery. Another alternative for extra battery life on the move is supplied by Griffin in the form of the TuneJuice, a plug in battery back up that will add up to 8 extra hours of playtime to your iPod.

The addition of Bluetooth to Apple's players is something that's speculated on every once in a while. But until the company adds it to its range, we'll have to rely on 3rd party manufacturers coming up with wireless goods. Icombi (www.icombi.com) is a company offering a Bluetooth adapter for your iPod. Rather than adding the wireless technology so that you can transfer tracks over from your computer, this Bluetooth functionality is strictly so you can listen to your music through wireless headphones, also available from Icombi.

Whatever new add or gadget you envisage for your iPod, you can be fairly certain that someone's already out there working on the prototype, or getting ready to market the finished article. It seems this group of portable hard drive players has been responsible for a creative wave that has spread across the world, and everywhere you turn there are products either created for, or directly inspired by Apple's iPod.

CHAPTER 13

Sony

The new Walkman range

Why did Sony miss out on the digital audio personal market and how does it plan to take on Apple? Introducing Sony's hard disk personals, key features of NW-HD3 and how to transfer tracks on to it and Sony's latest hard disk Walkman, the NW-HD5.

Sony
The new Walkman range

At the end of the seventies, Sony unveiled the Walkman and changed personal audio for ever. The first ever pocket music player had arrived. A decade or so later Sony once again re-invented music on the move, this time pioneering the CD Walkman.

In the early nineties Sony took personal audio to yet another dimension with the introduction of the MiniDisk - a digital audio player that offered much better sound than cassette but was a fraction of the size of CD players. Given its heritage in personal audio, you would have happily bet large sums of money that Sony would pioneer and dominate the digital audio market which began to emerge five or six years ago.

Sony certainly thought it was going to be a major player, delivering a large range of flash memory based Walkmans way before Apple and rivals like Dell and Philips had even thought of producing MP3 players. Yet, until the beginning of 2005, Sony has been trounced in the digital audio market not only by Apple, but by smaller companies like Creative and iRiver. In fact, for a while, it looked as if Sony had lost the personal audio player market forever. Much of the reason for Sony's failure to challenge rival Apple was down to what critics argued was short-sightedness on behalf of not only of its consumer electronics wing, but also its music and movie software divisions. Worried that the rise of MP3 would eat in CD sales, Sony initially refused to make its music players MP3-compatible, rather users had to convert MP3 files into its proprietary ATRAC format before they could port them from a PC to the player.

Sony was also very slow in embracing hard disks preferring instead to champion flash memory and in particular its own removable flash storage system, Memory Stick. Sony's reticence created a huge hole in the market which Apple, along with Creative,

Philips and countless others, were happy to fill. The first murmurings of a change in strategy came in 2004 when the company launched its music download service Connect and unveiled its first ever hard disk player - the NW-HD1.

There was no denying that this was a superb piece of hardware that had the edge over its rival the iPod in key areas like size and battery life. However users still had to convert their MP3 files to ATRAC before they could put them on the player which, if a user had a large collection of files, could take some time. Some users also complained that the software that accompanied the player, Sonic Stage, was full of bugs and kept crashing.

So Sony returned the drawing board and in December 2004 unveiled arguably its first credible crack at the hard disk player market – the NW-HD3. In terms of design, features and performance there was little difference between the NW-HD1 and the NW-HD3. The crucial change was that the new model could play MP3s. All users had to do was fire up the revamped SonicStage software, let it scour their hard disk for MP3 music files and then port them over to the new device. The NW-HD3 got excellent reviews and many critics argued that at last Sony was offering a real alternative to the iPod.

Then in spring 2005 Sony released its most important range of players so far. The new set included an excellent selection of flash memory based models designed to take the iPod shuffle on, and most important of all, the NW-HD5 its first true iPod rival. Sure there are still many compelling reasons to choose an iPod over an NW-HD5, but if you compare the HD5 with its 20 Gigabyte iPod equivalent, in several key areas the Sony model has the edge.

Quite where Sony will go in the future remains open to a great deal of conjecture. The company obviously has a heritage in video and has already debuted hard disk based video/audio players in Japan. Its next hard disk model is likely to boast all the features of the innovative HD5 as well as a color screen.

By the end of the year expect to see Sony and Apple colour screen 20 Gigabyte players battling it out. It will certainly be an interesting fight.

Sony
The new Walkman range

Sony NW-HD3

So, if you have chosen to go with Sony rather than Apple here's the low-down on the first of the two hard key hard disk players in the maker's range

Why buy the NW-HD3?
Apple might have larger market share but there are many critics who think that the NW-HD3 has the edge over its Apple rival in terms of superior hardware. The unit is smaller and lighter than its Apple rival and some would say more stylish with its ultra modern slate grey finish. The Sony has the edge in another key area too – battery life, while the 20 Gigabyte iPod needs recharging after 12 hours the NW-HD3 will play MP3 files for 20 hours – even longer if the user has chosen to encode their music in Sony's own ATRAC format. Given Sony's heritage in the personal audio market the NW-HD5 is a superb sounding player, certainly as good if not better than its Apple rival. In terms of hardware then the Sony would appear to have the edge. However Apple champions point to the iPod's iconic design, its simple to use scroll wheel, which is arguably a lot less tricky than the NW-HD3's four way rocker switch and select button, and the fact that the iPod is compatible with the iTunes music store, the most popular music download service in the world.

Another advantage Apple has over Sony is that its iTunes software is much more intuitive than the SonicStage system that accompanies Sony players. However Sony has improved the interface and the gap between the two systems is starting to narrow.

What's in the box?
There's earphones, a USB 2.0 connector, AC power adaptor and a pouch.

What audio formats does the NW-HD3 play?
It is obviously compatible with ATRAC3plus which is the latest version of Sony's own ATRAC audio software. This includes tracks that are ripped to ATRAC via the SonicStage software and music downloaded from Sony's Connect website. The HD3 will also playback MP3s, but is not compatible with rival formats like Windows Media Audio or Ogg Vorbis.

Transferring songs to the player
Users first have to install the Sonic Stage software which accompanies the NW-HD3. This then trawls the hard disk, rounding up any MP3 or ATRAC music files they might have. Then users plug the NW-HD3 into the PC – it will then appear as a

Sony NW-HD5

device in the 'Transfer' section of the software on the top right hand corner. The user highlights the track/album and click the arrow to transfer the music to the HD3.

How do I recharge the battery?
The NW-HD3 comes with an AC adapter that plugs into the electricity mains. Sadly, unlike some Apple players, it can't be charged via USB.

How do I browse for a song?
Press the mode button on the player and then you can browse via album, artist or genre.

How do I choose shuffle?
Press the menu button and then press the down key until you reach 'Play Mode', then press the right button and you can chose between shuffling tracks and press select when you reach the shuffle button

As this book goes to press Sony is to deliver its most sophisticated hard disk personal audio player so far – the NW-HD5. The player is marginally smaller and lighter than the NW-HD3 and feels as if it should contain a five Gigabyte hard disk rather than a 20 Gigabyte one. Sony has also enhanced the screen and jettisoned the rocker switch in favor of separate buttons. There have also been some neat tweaks including a feature on the menu that groups together all the track users uploaded to the player the last time they connected it and lets them access the tracks with the click of a button. The player's screen also has a neat trick in that it can be used in either portrait or landscape mode. The NW-HD5's killer feature though- apart from its size and design – could well prove to be its battery life. It offers around 30 hours of MP3 playback from one charge – 40 hours if the user opts for Sony's ATRAC format. Also the battery is removable and replaceable, with Sony promising that new batteries will be available cheaply from local shopping malls.

Overall the NW-HD5 is a superb digital music player, which has the edge over its equivalent 20 Gigabyte iPod. Although Apple is unlikely to let this situation remain unanswered for long.

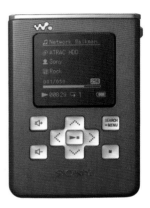

CHAPTER 14

Sony

Sony's flash memory players

Here, we investigate Sony's comprehensive range of Flash memory players, the sporty NW-E100, the NW-E400 series to rival the iPod shuffle and the top-end MP3-ATRAC-FM radio players, and discuss if the Sony flash memory Walkman is the right choice for you.

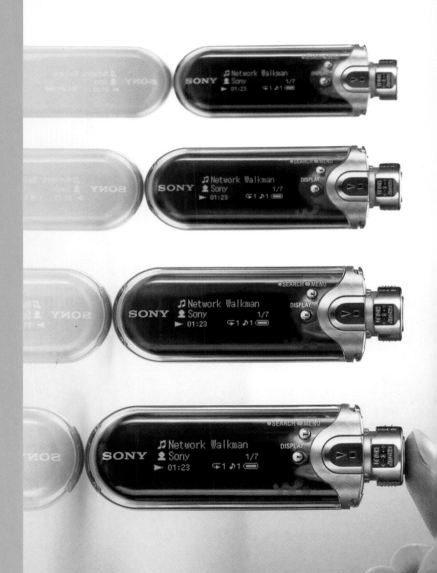

Sony
Flash memory players

While Apple and its iPod has stolen the digital music limelight, Sony has nevertheless been releasing a formidable collection of flash memory based music players. Some use its proprietary removable card storage system, Memory Stick, while other players have flash memory already built in.

Until recently, though, the players were often ignored by critics and punters, largely because they could not play MP3 files. Instead users had to convert the MP3 files into Sony's ATRAC format – a time-consuming and annoying process.

Sony argued that the transfer didn't alter the sound quality, though some consumers felt there was a clear loss of definition after the transfer had taken place.

Sony did, however, finally relent and, since the end of 2004, its flash memory players have been compatible with both MP3 and ATRAC files.

Sony has also benefited from renewed interest in the flash memory player market thanks mainly to its rival Apple and the release of its iPod shuffle. It gave

Sony an opportunity to launch models up against the shuffle, which, though slightly pricier than its Apple rivals, were much higher specified.

Another reason why Sony's flash memory players have started to attract more attention from buyers is that the storage capacity has started to increase significantly. When the players only offered 128MB of music they would only house around couple of hours of tunes.

Now that 1Gb players are available, consumers can choose flash memory products knowing that they have several hours of music to listen to.

There are currently three new types of Sony flash players available, so here is a quick whizz through what's on offer.

Previous page:
Arguably the best flash memory based models on sale the Sony NW-400 players are simple to use, very small and pocketable and boast an excellent quality OLED screen.

NW-E100

These are Sony's sporty players deigned to appeal to those who have an active lifestyle yet want colorful and fashionable players. The NW-E100 is available in three different guises: the E103, E105 and E107. They are essentially the same model other than their differing storage capacities; with the E103 boasting 256MB of music, the E105 having 512MB and the top end model, the E107 featuring one Gigabyte. Sony claims that the E107 can in fact store as many as 45CDs (but only if they are encoded as Sony ATRAC files, and not as MP3s).

Apart from the cute circular design and large storage capacities, the E100 series has two other key facilities. Firstly, unlike the iPod shuffle, the players sport an LCD window to enable users to refer to song, artist, or album titles while listening to music.

Perhaps more importantly, the players have astonishing battery life as they are able to run for 70 hours when listening to ATRAC files, from a single AAA alkaline battery.

If you are looking for an inexpensive yet robust flash memory and don't want to have to worry about recharging batteries the NW-E100 series is well worth considering.

NW-E400

The E400 is arguably Sony's big push in the flash memory digital audio market, designed to show that it can create small, yet inexpensive, models that can accommodate a lot of features and yet still perform superbly. Although there are many users who prefer the iPod shuffle, and others who favor models from Rio and Creative, the E400 is the flash player to own.

At first glance it looks to have quite an odd design with its rectangular, lozenge-shaped body and the funny-looking cap on top. Don't let the design put you off, though, for in terms of usability it makes perfect sense. The player is available in a several different colors with the user able to choose from black, red, green and blue.

Once again Sony has made a big feature of the screen with the NW-400 series models also sporting a very cool OLED (Organic Light Emitting Diode) display. This delivers basic information such as track and artist detail as well as enabling the user to control the player's volume and method of play (standard or random).

It works with the dial at the top of the player which, after it has been pulled up, enables the user to move

Sony
Flash memory players

from one track to another. When the user has finished making amendments, with one push, the dial clicks back into position and then acts as a hold button preventing the user from accidentally altering any controls.

In addition to the smart screen, Sony has ensured that the E400 players run for a very long time. Battery life from the supplied rechargeable unit is fifty hours if the user opts for ATRAC files, forty hours if they use MP3. Another really cool feature of the model is that it can deliver up to three hours of playback from a three-minute charge, which is really handy if a person needs to charge a player very quickly.

Just the like the other Sony flash memory players, the NW-E400 series models connect to a PC via their integrated USB sockets. In this instance the user peels off a small piece of plastic protection from the socket, which is sited at the bottom of the model. Once the player is connected to a USB socket it begins charging – it doesn't come with an AC adapter and this is only way to power it.

Tracks are transferred to the model via Sony's SonicStage software. Similarly to Sony's hard disk devices, this involves the user highlighting a track/album/playlist and the clicking on the transfer arrow to port it across.

While the players are compatible with both MP3 and ATRAC files, they will not play WMA tracks, nor are they compatible with the AAC tracks downloaded from Apple's iTunes online music store. Users can however transfer tracks in the ATRAC format which have been downloaded from Sony's iTunes rival Connect.

The models come in three different guises; the NW-E403, which has 256MB of storage, the NW-E405 which features 512MB, and the top of the range NW-E407 which has a one Gigabyte capacity.

NW-E500

If a Gigabyte of music still isn't enough for you, Sony also has a third range of flash memory players that also include an FM radio tuner.

The players are fairly similar to the NW-E400 models, though they come in different colors (namely silver, blue, gold and pink). Everything else, from the fifty hour battery playback (including the quick three minute charge facility) through to the three line OLED display, is the same. The models are available in 256MB (NW-E503), 512MB (NW-E505) and one gigabyte (NW-E505) versions.

Why buy a Sony flash memory Walkman?

While they are up against some pretty serious competition the Sony Network Walkman flash players do stand out for several reasons.

In terms of sound quality they are easily the equal of other players, they also score well in ease of use, thanks to their on-board screens.

But the main reason to buy a Sony model is battery life, as these players soldier on long after their rival models have given up.

If you are looking for an inexpensive compact player, with top sound quality, the battery life alone means you should consider the Sony models.

CHAPTER 15

The rivals

Creative, iriver and Rio

Now we turn our attention to Apple's and Sony's rivals, introducing Creative's players and Rio's flash- and hard disk-based players and iriver's range of personal audio players.

The rivals
Creative, iriver and Rio

Apple and Sony may be the best-known digital music player brands around, but Creative, iriver and Rio come in pretty close behind. The three companies have a history of producing popular and innovative players that offer a real alternative to Apple's range.

And while Apple has only recently moved into the flash player market, Creative, iRiver and Rio have been producing flash players in tandem with their hard disk drive players for a long time.

Creative

Although Creative has built up quite a portfolio of players, the company's flagship range is currently the hard drive Zen and the Zen Micro.

Previous players, such as the Zen Touch and Jukebox Zen, all varied in style, color and shape, and it's only with these latest players that the company has stuck to the same basic design, giving them more of a permanent look and feel that Apple has managed

to accomplish with its iconic iPod range. The other variants are still available for the time being, but the flagship Zen and Zen Micro design seems to be here to stay for the foreseeable future.

The main Zen player is a 20GB model that replaces the company's previous 20GB offerings. It's a far sleeker look and feel to some of the earlier models, many of whichhave been accused of being too bulky and cumbersome to offer a true alternative to the iPod players.

The Zen is in actual fact modeled on the smaller Zen Micro, and it has a far less rigid and a more rounded and relaxed look than other Zen players.

Whereas the iPod relies on the unique touch wheel for controlling its recent models, other companies

Previous page:
Creative's Zen Micro has been one of the most popular MP3 players of the last couple of years. It has a sleek design, solid amount of storage and very impressive line up of facilities. It is also compatible with the Napster To Go service.

Right:
Creative's Zen is one of the most popular models available and comes with a 20 Gigabyte hard disk.

have had to find alternative solutions to the problem of controlling and accessing so many songs in such a small device. Creative's solution is its vertical touch pad, which lets you scroll up and down through a menu list with relative ease. It comes with a blue screen, so you won't be able to view your digital pictures, but for a player of this size and capacity that's pretty much the same as similarly specified devices.

One of the major selling points of the Creative range is their compatibility with the Napster To Go service, which lets you pay a set fee each month in return to full access to the Napster music library.

Being able to download and play music from the entire catalogue makes the Zen seem an appealing prospect, and with dimensions that match up pretty well to the iPod 20GB, this offers a true alternative that some users will finding tempting.

Extra features are also in place to lure away iPod's potential customers. As well as a voice recorder, the Zen includes an FM radio receiver, so you can listen to your favorite shows on the go, and the facility to record what you're listening to straight onto your player.

It's not all good news, however. Battery life is quoted at just 11 hours of playback. This may have compared favorably with the iPods a few months back, but since Apple has released its latest, fourth Generation iPod, even its battery life has gone up to 12 hours – and in fact some reviews are quoting more than that in their tests.

The other hero of the Creative camp is the Zen Micro, the closest thing Creative has to an iPod mini rival. Obviously working with the view that more equals better, Creative has outdone the mini's selection of four different color options, releasing the Zen Micro in 10 different colors: dark blue, light blue, white, black, red, pink, orange, green, purple and gray.

As well as being spoilt for choice on the color front, you'll also find a number of extra features that don't appear on the mini. For starters, you can take your pick from 4, 5 or 6GB capacities, although the 5GB seems to be the one that's most readily available.

Like its larger-sized sibling, the Micro includes an FM radio that you can record onto the player and a voice recorder for taking notes.

It also has the benefit of including a removable battery which means you'll not only be able to replace it when it gets past its best, you'll also be

The rivals
Creative, iriver and Rio

able to buy a spare to charge for long journeys. And you'll probably want to do that, because while you'll get up to 18 hours from a single charge of a mini, a Micro will only provide you with 12.

Like the 20GB Zen, the Micro has a vertical trackpad for controlling the functions and a clear, bright, blue screen for displaying track information. Again, the inclusion of compatibility with Napster's To Go service is likely to be a pull for many consumers and with a sturdy design and compact feel, the Micro offers a reasonably attractive alternative to the iPod mini.

Both of these players can be synchronized with your Windows Outlook, so you'll be able to catch up on emails, check out your latest diary appointments and consult your contacts address book wherever you are. And while players from Sony and Apple require software to move files across from your hard drive, you have the option of using the Zen players like external storage media, which means you can drag and drop music straight onto the player. Alternatively, you can use the supplied Zen Media Explorer or you can synchronize with the excellent Windows Media Player 10.

Rio

As the company that released one of the first MP3 players on the market, Rio has certainly had the time to hone and perfect its range. And it's probably the reason that Rio's players look so different from the rest of the field, without many of the telltale signs of Apple-inspired design.

The company's hard drive players all look pretty much the same, with the same near-square body that makes them eminently pocketable. Currently, the company has a relatively small selection of hard drive players, with the ce2100 offering 2.5GB of storage and the Rio Carbon players offering 5 and 6GB of memory. Colors are fairly limited as well, with a black ce2100 and Carbons available in a silvery finish and the newer "Pearl" variety.

It's not till your hold the Rio Carbon Pearl 5GB in your hand that you realize just how slight it is. Photos of the player don't really do it justice, and the narrowness of the player, which tapers to an even slimmer bottom, is only really appreciated once you have hold of it. Comparing it to the iPod mini leaves the mini looking rather large and cumbersome, and the Rio can also safely match the mini for build quality and unique design – something that can't be

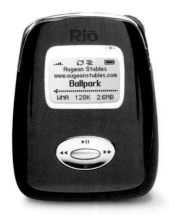

Above:
The Rio range of Carbon and ce1200 players are incredibly thin for models boasting hard disks.

said for a lot of the competitor players out there.But this slim design does come at a price.You won't find this 5GB player packed with the extra features you find on the Creative Zen Micro, for example.There's no FM radio, no photo viewer and no removable battery, but if you're looking for something that's lightweight and desirable, you'll probably be willing to forgo these little extras without too much of a wrench.One thing the Carbon does include, however, is a voice recorder, so you'll be able to take notes and record meetings or lectures straight onto the player.

The Rio is missing Apple's tactile touchwheel or Creative's trackpad, but the scroll wheel on the top right side of the player works just as well, providing fast and convenient access to tracks as well as doubling as a volume control.There's also the front faceplate for controlling the player if you prefer, which allows you to move between tracks and control the play settings.And if you're in the middle of listening to a tune or audio book and need to stop for any reason, the Rio can bookmark your place for you so that you can resume where you left off next time you use it.

With support for WMA tracks along with MP3 and Audible files you'll have a good selection to choose

from.You can move tunes to your player using the highly usable Rio Music Manager software or the Windows Media Player 10 synchronization tool. Or, if you prefer, you can drag and drop music straight onto the player, making the Rio, like the Creative Zen players, a very versatile option. And one that is easily a match for the Apple iPod mini.

But the company hasn't just made a name for itself producing hard drive players, and there's a strong line of flash players to choose from as well. Just as the hard drive players all use a similar design, the flash devices are all based round the same basic chassis as well.

The main focus of the Rio flash players is their suitability for sport and most of them carry "Sport" in their name somewhere.The Rio Forge Sport range are the most

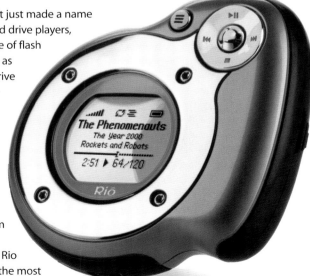

The rivals
Creative, iriver and Rio

well-known of the players, available in 128MB, 256MB and 512MB capacities. These come in small, stylish, and rugged bodies with protective rubber trim and a tough, stainless steel faceplate. They include sport-friendly features such as a lap timer and stopwatch and also come with FM radios that can be recorded straight to the player's memory. Further temptation is provided by the inclusion of a memory card slot, which lets you plug in a Secure Digital card up to 1GB in size to add extra storage space.

iriver

Like both Creative and Rio, iriver has managed to attract its fair share of supporters. Its highly usable and cost effective H300 series may not have had the style or iconic appeal of the Apple players, but all those extra features combined with a realistic price tag has made iriver a force to be reckoned with on the hard drive player market. And now the company is back with a new range that has design more firmly at its heart than previous players. The H10 20GB color player has recently been announced as a replacement for the H300 series.

Just as Creative has brought the designs of its

players into the same basic chassis, iriver has created a range of players all under the same H10 moniker that all look and feel pretty much the same. The new H10 20GB is very similar to the already-established 5GB H10 and a tiny 1GB flash version is also due to hit the stores soon. This serves to provide iriver with a stronger brand that can compete more effectively with the dominance of Apple's unified iPod lineup.

Just how much you like the design that iriver has gone for is really down to personal preference. There's a greater selection of colors on offer, with red, blue, silver and gray to choose from in all the capacities. There's less metal on show than on the Rio, Sony and Apple players, and some may find the casings a little too plastic for their liking. The trackpad might look familiar to Creative users as well, since their players also use the feature. Sliding your finger up and down the panel will scroll you through the menu options.

As well as giving the player designs an overhaul, iriver has made another very important change to it's the H10 range. For many, the beauty of the H300 series was that they didn't support ID3 tags (not without a very labor-intensive scanning process, at least) and that therefore you didn't need to worry about Digital Rights Management on your music.

What this meant in terms of use was that transferring tracks to the player was best left to simple drag and drop from the music files on your computer.

Now, iriver has decided to make life easier for the majority of consumers and the H10s support ID3 tags. This means you'll now be able to use Windows Media Player 10 to organize your tunes, as well as iriver's own iriver Plus software. You can still use drag and drop if you prefer to do that, however.

When it comes to setting itself apart from the crowd, the H10 has piled on the features, making it a player suited to those who like to make the most of their portable hard drive.

The color screens that are included on all three capacities are the players' main selling point, providing ample opportunity for photo fans to view and store their images. The large screens are high resolution across the range so you can check out slideshows of your photos or read text books and files while your music is playing in the background.

There is also an FM radio which you can record straight onto the player, and a voice recorder with built-in mic which, unlike many other players out there, encodes your sound files to MP3 format instead of the WAV/AIFF format used on CDs.

The Line In and Line Out connectors found on the H300 series have been relegated to the dock now, which means you won't just be able to plug your player straight into your hi-fi using Line Out or connect up a more powerful microphone. So make sure you get a cradle if you want to use those extra features.

Because the H10 range is still fairly new in the player market, it's hard to say just how much of a threat it will pose to the dominance of the Apple players, but having a line up that's united in a common design certainly makes the iriver brand stronger on the outside. And with the lure of a color screen across the range, many consumers are going to find the H10 players very tempting prospects indeed.

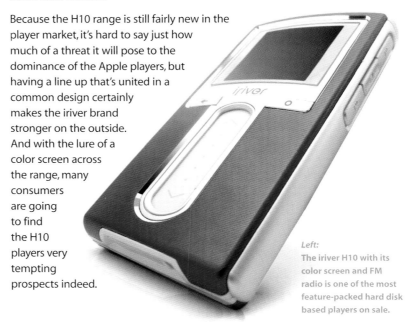

Left:
The iriver H10 with its color screen and FM radio is one of the most feature-packed hard disk based players on sale.

CHAPTER 16

Other brands

Dell, Samsung and Cowon

This is where we examine what else is on offer, Dell's extensive range of personal audio players for example, and discuss how Samsung intends to take on Apple and why Cowon is the best music player manufacturer you've never heard of.

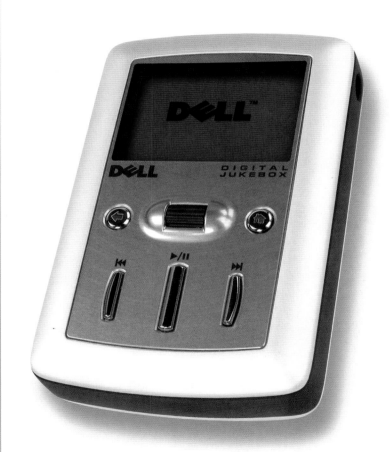

Other brands
Dell, Samsung and Cowon

Although we've covered the most major brands of players out there, there are a fair few excellent players on the market from other manufacturers.

Many of the less well-known MP3 player companies are unlikely to take on the might of Apple or Sony and win, simply because they can't compete at the same level – and can't always produce compelling enough products to steal the limelight.

It's likely that in the future some of the very small competitors will eventually fade into the background, unable to gain enough of a market share to make the digital music market viable for them. But companies such as Dell, Samsung and Cowon, who have managed to create a strong portfolio of products, there's a good opportunity for them to poach some of the custom from the major players

Dell and Samsung of course have the advantage of already having a large and well established base in the electronics community with other products. This makes it easier for them to command some brand loyalty among their established customers. Samsung, for example, has a large following in the

Far East – especially its home country of Korea where it makes everything from televisions to motor cars – while Dell can draw on its experience within the computer and PDA market.

Cowon's emergence onto the music scene may have seemed to have come from nowhere, but the Korean company has quickly made a name for itself in the West thanks to a very strong line up of players that impressed from the outset.

The digital music market is still some way away from reaching saturation, and there are plenty of customers still out there who have yet to be wooed into to the digital age.

So for the meantime, there's space enough to accommodate the many manufacturers, large and small, that continue to pump ever-more innovative, ever-more compact and ever-cheaper devices into the shops and online stores.

Right:
Dell's DJ range of players are among the most popular models in the US.

Dell

Dell is currently selling its hard drive player range in the US, and doing very well out of it. The DJ range includes a 30GB DJ 30, 20BG DJ 20 and 5GB Pocket DJ player, which makes it a match for Apple's standard 20GB iPod and 5GB minis. All three players are based around the same silver design, which includes three, silver, vertical control buttons and a front scroll barrel flanked by two further control buttons on either side.

The blue screen is present on all the players, making then unsuitable for viewing photos, but good enough for finding your tracks. It's proved a popular design, that is both minimalist and functional, and it has avoided the negative comparisons many players get with the iPod design by virtue of being different enough.

There's support for MP3 and WAV files, as well as Windows' DRM-protected WMA files. This means you'll be able to synch it with Windows Media Player for transferring and organizing your tunes.

A major selling point for many will be the player's compatibility with Napster's subscription service, Napster To Go, which provides access to the entire Napster music library for a set monthly fee.

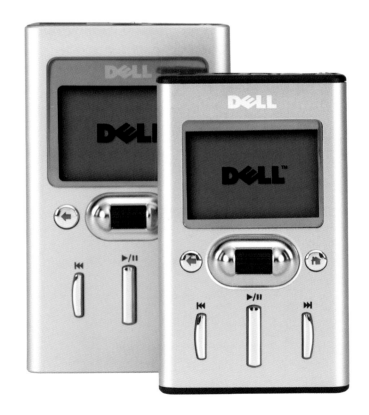

Other brands
Dell, Samsung and Cowon

All three players carry basically the same features, with nothing particularly to differentiate the larger players from the smaller – except for the casing sizes. Dell has made sure that the 20GB DJ works out nearly $50 cheaper than the 20GB iPod, while the price tag of the 5GB Pocket DJ is comparable to the 4GB iPod mini. This is likely to win it some custom for those looking to save a bit of money. But because there aren't really any extra features – no radio, no picture viewer, no voice recorder – you might feel a little cheated of those neat add-ons.

If you're someone who's just looking for something to store and play your tunes on, however, and you're not interested in using your portable hard drive player for anything more, the DJ range could well be worth checking out.

Samsung

Over in Korea Samsung is constantly announcing new and ever-smaller flash players to add to its Yepp range. While some of them make their way over to the Western market, a lot of them remain firmly on the Far Eastern market, leaving us to look on in envy. The players that we do get to see are split into two different camps: the YH range, hard drive players; and the YP range, smaller flash players.

As is often the case, the YP flash range outnumbers the hard drive YH range. However, on closer investigation you soon learn that many of the players with different names are identical apart from colors or capacities. The YP Flash range include the YP-MT6 series, a standard flash player that comes with a line-in port and FM radio; the tiny YP-T5 range, Samsung's smallest flash player that comes with a pretty basic feature set but does include an FM stereo; and the YP-60V, Samsung's tough sport player that includes a heart rate monitor, calorie counter and stop watch as well as an FM radio.

But probably Samsung's most notable flash player is the YP-T7X, a flash player with picture viewer. It comes with 512MB of storage space and a color screen that's large enough for you to view JPEG

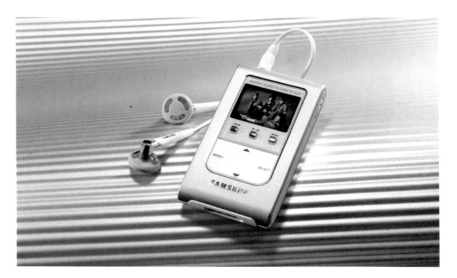

digital pictures and text files. Music formats it supports include MP3, WMA (including those with DRM encoding) and ASF, while an FM radio lets you listen to and record radio shows. There's also a voice recording facility and a clock that lets you set an alarm or program, making this a fairly feature-rich player for a flash audio device.

The Samsung hard drive range isn't quite so packed with selection as the YP flash range, with the company preferring to focus its attention on just a few players. The YH-920 is probably its best known player, thanks in part to the inclusion of Napster in its name. To give it its full title, the YH-920 Napster HDD player has been officially branded with the Napster logo, providing some added kudos to the portable audio player. In fact all the Samsung players are compatible with Napster, which means that users can take advantage of the company's To Go subscription service.

The player itself is a second generation device, with its predecessor also having the benefit of the Napster logo across its front. It comes with 20GB of memory, which puts it in line with Apple's standard iPod. MP3, WMA and Secure WMA files are all supported, but it's worth noting that you'll need to have Windows XP on your computer in order to use the 920. An FM tuner is included which also has the facility to let you record shows directly onto your player, while a Line In connector means you can encode audio straight onto the player as well. There's no color screen for viewing images; instead you get a backlit blue display, and a battery life that's quoted at just 10 hours puts this near the bottom of the pile when it comes to power. But it's

Above:
Samsung's YH-820 is an iPod mini rival. Its is smaller and lighter than the Apple player and it also boasts a striking color screen.

Other brands
Dell, Samsung and Cowon

easy to use and the Napster service, which is supplied free for two months, is likely to appeal to a lot of people.

The 920 has recently been joined by two color players, which offer the added attraction of photo viewers. The YH-820MC Micro HDD Jukebox is a direct competitor to the iPod mini players, providing 5GB of storage capacity with room for up to 1200 songs. Once again, battery life is pretty poor, with just 8 hours of playback time.

The YH-925GS is an upgrade of the Napster 920, without its predecessor's branding. It comes with a color screen for viewing your photos or album art and the 20GB hard disk drive has space for up to 5000 songs on it. It doesn't have a direct competitor in the iPod camp because the color screen places it above the standard iPod 20GB, but its capacity leaves it flagging in the face of the iPod photo 30GB. Battery life is better than the 820, but the same as the 920 at just 10 hours.

Cowon

Cowon is, like Samsung, a Korean company. But unlike Samsung, Cowon first sprung to prominence in the West almost solely thanks to its digital audio devices, and since it released its first iPod alternative it has found a good number of fans among consumers.

As with so many of the flash player manufacturers out there, Cowon has a pretty large portfolio of players that offer pretty much the same set list of features and functions, but which distinguish themselves with unusual extras such as design, affordability or size. First in the range is the iAudio 5, a basic 256MB/512MB/1GB player that comes in a selection of chassis and screen colors and offers 20 hours of playback for MP3, WMA, OGG and WAV music files. The iAudio G3 boasts 50 hours of music playback from just one AA battery, apparently making it one of the most power-friendly players on the market. Again, it's available in 256MB, 512MB and 1GB capacities and can support MP3, WMA, OGG, and WAV files. Voice recording is present, as is an FM radio that you can record straight onto the player. The iAudio U2 is a popular player that has garnered much attention and admiration for its good looks and small size. It comes with a built-in

Lithium-polymer rechargeable battery that Cowon claims will run for a very respectable 20 hours. It's got a number of innovative little features, such as the logo design application, JetLogo, that lets you create your own animated logo to display on your screen. JetEffect offers more than the usual selection of equalizer settings for flash players, with 6 pre-configured settings and numerous sound effects. It also offers FM radio and recording, direct audio encoding which means you can record voice notes or any other sound, and support for WMA, MP3, OGG and WAV music files.

The iAudio CW300 is the company's more classic model, using a metallic chassis that gives it a high end feel. The iAudio CW200 is a smaller player, but it also comes with an aluminum casing for added durability. And finally, there's the iAudio 4, a small aluminum player with a fun extra feature. The LCD panel that displays track and album information offers 124 backlight LED colors. This means that the player's screen will change color while you're using it. You can set these colors however you like – for example, you could have a specific color for MP3 playback, and another color for FM radio. Themes can be set up to create different color displays, which means that colors will change dynamically as you use your player and listen to your music.

But it's not the flash players that made Cowon's name: its hard drive players were the things that got it noticed. The current model is the iAudio M3, a hard drive player that looks quite unlike similar models in its field. It still uses that upright, rectangular design that most players use, but its silver casing is almost entirely bereft of features, making it a minimalist unit quite unlike the others. Sleek and slim line, with a brushed metal finish that will appeal to many, but this design is not without its compromises. For starters, there's no screen on the main body of the unit. Instead, it's been relegated to the earphone remote control unit. While this makes for a big remote control, it's still a small screen by current standards and you won't be able to use the blue LCD for viewing photos or reading text files. Extra features include an FM stereo that you can record straight onto the player, voice recorder with built in microphone and support for MP3, OGG, WMA, WAV and FLAC files. The iAudio M3 comes in a choice of 20GB or 40GB capacities. If you can live without the screen, you'll find the superslim design very appealing indeed.

CHAPTER 17

Unusual stuff

Odd music players

Now for some weird places you can put your MP3 player, players you can take swimming, players that double as sunglasses, players you can wear as jewelry, players built into watches and headphones, and players to accompany an active lifestyle.

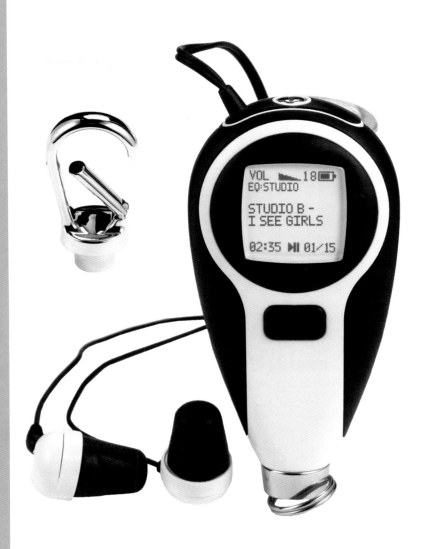

Unusual stuff
Odd music players

It's not taken manufacturers long to realize that if you can put flash memory into an object then you can make it MP3 compatible. And flash memory being the versatile storage type it is, you can put it into pretty much anything. And people have.

With the result that there are now more weird and wonderful MP3-enabled products out there than most people would ever imagine. Everything from watches, to cameras; teddy bears to sunglasses: you'll find them all out there somewhere. Often, these sorts of products are the sole preserve of the Far Eastern market, with only customers in Japan, Korea and the other neighboring countries getting the full benefit of some of these innovative – or just plain idiotic items.

But it's not all bad news for us – the odd item does find its way over here – and there are products being made for the American and European markets, so we're not entirely limited in our choices. If you're looking for something specific or unusual, chances are it's out there somewhere already and if not, it probably soon will be.

Waterproof players

Oregon Scientific has only made serious moves into the MP3 market in recent times, but has distinguished itself from the crowd by coming up with a number of unusual and inventive products.

The tiny MP100 flash player is one of the world's smallest, coming in a variety of colors and capacities of up to 512MB. But it's the MP120 that really steals the limelight, offering consumers an entirely waterproof music player that they can take swimming, rowing, or sailing, without fear of damage. As well as offering waterproof music playback for up to a meter down, the MP120 is also shockproof to protect it from knocks and bumps. The earphones are also waterproof – although only when they're

Previous page:
MP3 players that are so waterproof you can take them swimming are starting to catch on. Oregon Scientific's MP-120 is one of the best models available.

Above:
The Oakley Thump is a pair of shades with an integrated MP3 player

securely inserted into your ears – which means that you'll be able to get in the water as soon as you take the player out of its box. It's available with up to 512MB of storage capacity and includes an FM radio and a built in rechargeable battery that should provide up to 16 hours of music playback.

There's support for both MP3 and WMA files, and an LCD screen that displays the ID3 tag information. Over in the UK, Ministry of Sound also has a waterproof MP3 player that offers similar features, but doesn't have a shockproof casing though adds a note taking facility so you can record sound files.

Oakley Thump

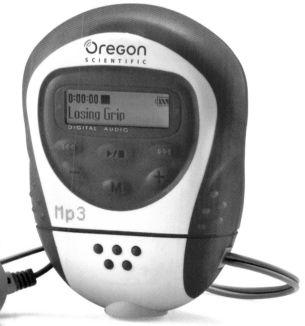

It seems hard to believe that a company ever came up with the idea of turning a pair of sunglasses into a portable music player, but the fact that they not only came up with the idea, they also went ahead and manufactured them for sale to the public seems almost impossible to believe. Oakley, a company more usually associated with the fashion industry, not the electronics industry, has designed a set of sunglasses that incorporate a music player. Oakley is calling its Thump shades the "world's first digital eyewear". The player itself is built into the side of the frame, with slightly enlarged sides helping to disguise its presence. The short earphones are encased in matching plastic, with only the very end buds on show, which can be altered to fit. Unlike many music players, the Thump shades don't rely on in-ear earbuds to produce the sound. Instead, the player uses small speakers, which can be adjusted so

Unusual stuff
Odd music players

that they float right next to your ear without having to be pushed right inside. The control buttons are located on the two arms, which keeps everything wire-free and tidy and the plastic frame has been designed to be as lightweight as possible, leaving it highly portable but a little flimsy feeling as well.

Luckily, it has shock control built in, so you shouldn't have too many problems if you drop the Thump, and the frame will fit pretty securely on your head anyway. Oakley has also thought about those times when you might want to listen to music, but don't want the polarized lenses, and so these can be flipped up and out of the way while you're indoors or in poor light.

There's a variety of colors and to choose from, and you'll find 128MB and 256MB versions capable of playing MP3s, WAVs and DRM-protected WMA files, so you'll be able to purchase music from most download stores.

The small capacities may put some people off, but with a choice of simply dragging and dropping files, or pairing the player with Windows Media Player, you'll be able to update your selection fairly regularly. Unsurprisingly, there aren't any extra features on this audio device, but then again, having a casing that's also a set of sunglasses is probably enough of a feature for most people. These certainly aren't shades that most women would want to wear, since even with their lightweight design, they're still pretty large frames – and not particular feminine-looking either.

Jewelry

Luckily, if you're a girl who likes things a bit more feminine, there are products out there for you. iriver was certainly thinking of the female market when it developed the N10 player. This tiny audio device has been designed to resemble a pendant so that it can be worn around the neck like jewelry. The earphones are incorporated into the necklace design, and can be clipped onto the rest of the neck strap or plugged into your ears as you desire.

When the player's not in use, the screen takes on a mirrored appearance, making it look even more like a jewelry pendant. And, in fact, if you want to you, you can unclip the earphone neckstrap and attach the N10 to the alternative earphone-free neckstrap that comes in the box, making it even more like a piece of jewelry and even less like a music player.

Despite its small size and lightweight design, iriver

Left:
The iRiver N10 is designed to be worn as jewelry. It is one of the most striking flash memory based players on sale.

has somehow managed to cram up to 512MB of storage onto the player (with a 1GB version already available in Korea).

There's a battery life that should last for 11 hours of music playback, a voice recorder with built in microphone, and a built-in rechargeable lithium polymer battery. And iriver's not the only company to see jewelry as a good fit for digital audio.

BenQ is another manufacturer to release a pendant player. It's hard to believe how tiny the Joybee 102R is, but the player really is small enough to pass for a round stone pendant.

It's made from plastic and comes in a number of swirling and colorful designs. You won't find many features on board – there's no screen and you basically have to listen to each track in turn – but it's a fun player that many will appreciate.

Because of its small stature, the sound quality is no match for some of the larger, better specified players on the market, but as far as music players masquerading as jewelry go, this one does a pretty successful job of both. It comes in 64MB, 128MB and 256MB capacities, plays MP3, WMA and WAV audio files, and offers up to 10 hours' battery life from its rechargeable in-built battery.

Unusual stuff
Odd music players

Watches

Watches have also become popular receptacles for the technology, with a fair selection now appearing for sale. A number of them, from the likes of Evergreen and Thanko, are only available in the Far East – or on import from a couple of American and European gadget importers. But you will find some available for sale from manufacturers active in the West. Somewhat ironically, most of these watches tend to be analog designs, rather than digital faces, and while there are a couple that come in heavier metal bodies, most are plastic or rubber sports-style watches.

Aigo is one company that sells its products in the North American and European market. It has a selection of different watches to choose from in varying styles. The UW-F022 is a colorful watch available in blue or red clear plastic. It supports MP3 and WMA files, and also incorporates a digital voice recorder with built in microphone. It's both shock proof and static proof and you can use it as a standard flash storage device, loading photos and files and any other digital data you like onto the memory. The UW-F021 is very similar, providing playback for MP3 and WMA files, and incorporating a digital voice recorder. Protection against shock and static, as well as a

standard data storage facility for non-music files are all here as well. In fact, the only real difference is the style of the watch, which comes with a black strap, with silver rim and black analogue faceplate. It's available in 128MB and 256MB capacities.

Finally, there's the UW-E011, the sleekest and slimmest of the three watches. It comes in a stylish black and silver design, with a simple, black, analog fascia with large silver numbers. There's space for up to 512MB of memory, and as with the other watch players in the range, the UW-E011 will work as a standard USB memory drive as well as playing MP3 and WMA files. There's no voice recording facility on this watch, which perhaps explains the slimmer design, but it does have protection against static and shocks. Whether you'd ever want to wear one of these watch players really comes down to how odd you'd feel wearing earphones plugged into your wristwatch. But with technologies improving all the time, these timepieces are getting slimmer and slimmer. Plus, the improvements in Bluetooth wireless means that there should soon be a watch player that offers wire-free connection to your headphones, allowing you to go about your day unencumbered by cables.

Headphones

Alternatively, you could just opt for a music player that comes built into your headphones. JVC is one company producing a set of earphones that include a digital player.

The XA-A50 headphones are similar to many modern sets, offering over ear loops that hold them in place, with soft cables running behind the neck to join the headset together. The actual speaker casings themselves are bulkier than you'd usually get, though, since they house the flash memory and battery.

There's just 128MB of memory on board, which is poor compared to many other modern players, but which is enough to give you 30 MP3 files or 60 WMA files. WMA files with Digital Rights Management (DRM) included can also be played, which means you can synchronize the XA-A50 with Windows Media Player. You should get a reported 20 hours of music playback from the one AAA battery stored within the headset. Control buttons are located on the right ear, and you can also use the Voice Guidance facility to control your player when you're wearing it.

And JVC isn't the only company producing all-in-one solutions. TDK's MOJO 1, based on the same

principles as the XA-A50 but with a slightly different feature set. For starters, the design, while remaining a behind-neck set up, offers a stiff headband and a basic over ear loop to rest the speakers into place.

There's also the added attraction of a built in FM radio, which means you'll be able to continue listening after you've been through all your own digital tracks.

Unusual stuff
Odd music players

Memory is slightly less of a problem on the MOJO 1 headphones, however, because while it too only comes with 128MB of internal memory, the presence of a Secure Digital/MultiMediaCard slot in the headphones means you'll be able to upgrade the storage capacity and carry spare cards with you to change playlists on the move. You can also record radio straight onto the player's internal memory.

All the features can be accessed via the button controls on the sides of the headphones, and you should get 10 hours of music playback from the single AAA battery.

You might find yourself missing an LCD screen, but being able to move about without wires will appeal to many people – especially those constantly on the move such as runners, cyclists or other sports enthusiasts.

Sport Players

Bringing us neatly to the next unusual category … We've already mentioned a couple of sports players and, indeed, many of the flash player manufacturers, such as Rio, have made it clear how well-suited their players are for sport lovers. But even these have been standard players, often just with shock absorbing features, and rubberized grips.

When Nike teamed up with Philips, they decided to go for something a little bit more unusual for their sport players. The MP3Run from Nike-Philips is a 256MB, rounded flash player, with the usual rubber edging and protective casing you expect on sports players. But it also comes with an added extra: a further unit attaches to your shoe, measuring your footfalls to let you know how far you've run.

This pedometer unit connects to your music player via wireless Bluetooth, sending data to the player over the air. You can then gain audible feedback, with details of your distances delivered by a synthesized voice to your earphones.

Once home, you can download all the data that your pedometer sent to your player, creating graphs and charts of your running progress on the Nike Run website. The player also comes with an FM radio if you get tired of the MP3 and WMA tracks you've saved, and Nike-Philips have also thoughtfully included a strobe light for you to switch on when the light grows poor for extra safety.

Left:
Philips and Nike have a range of models including the MP3 Run which sports an unusual round design.

Music playing Phones

Are they the future?

What about the mobile phone? Will it beat the iPod? It certainly makes sense to carry around one gadget and not two but there are issues regarding the battery life. We'll take you through downloading music direct to your mobile, storage, music video and more

Music playing phones
Are they the future?

In October 2001 at an Apple press conference company CEO Steve Jobs plucked a small white box from his pocket and gave the world its very first glimpse of the iPod. While other manufacturers like Creative had delivered hard disk based MP3 players, none could match the iconic design, quality performance and superb software support of the new player.

Yet, a few months before, a product had been unveiled which has since largely been forgotten about, but historians may eventually rate in terms of innovation as being just as important as the iPod.

The product was the Siemens SL45 – the first phone capable of playing MP3s. It probably has slipped from people's consciousness largely because it had just 32MB of memory – space for around half an hour of tunes – and a battery that packed up after less than an hour of music.

Yet fast forward a decade from now, and chances are the music people listen to on the move will be supplied by a device that looks a lot more like the SL45 than the iPod. By the end of 2005 the music

playing cellphone is certain to be big news. Nokia has already lined up a phone that has the same music storage capacity as the low-end Apple iPod mini, while Sony Ericsson has its own Walkman-branded music-playing handset.

Aware that a new market could be emerging, even Apple has been working with Motorola on a phone that is compatible with its iTunes software that will also play back music downloaded from its website

In the UK, and most of Europe, cellphone operators are also are taking advantage of the faster data speeds of the new 3G services to offer music downloads over the air direct to handsets. This might not be huge at the moment, but given the

Previous page:
Sony Ericsson's W800 is the first mobile/cellphone to feature the Walkman branding.

Above:
Nokia's N91 mobile phone, which launches at the end of the 2005, can be bought with a wireless headset.

way in which the downloaded ringtone has become enormously popular in Europe it is very likely to develop into a huge business.In fact even people are already starting to carry music on their cellphone already. Thanks to the drop in the price of flash memory cards the amount of music people can cart round with them on their phone has also skyrocketed with several hours of music now available relatively cheaply. For the phone to truly rival the iPod and its rival devices as a music player, the mobile will have to evolve in certain key ways.

Below:
Nokia's 7710 phone not only features music playback facilities, some European versions of the phone will soon be able to tune into digital TV.

One gadget, not two

Firstly phone manufacturers will need to convince consumers that they only really need to take one gadget with them - their phone. The second issue facing phone makers is being able to offer a similar amount of storage to devices like the iPod.

Yet perhaps the most difficult problem manufacturers face is the phone's limited battery life. The 20 Gigabyte iPod currently offers twelve hours of playback before it shuts down. Phone batteries can't rival this at the moment and, besides music, batteries will also have TV tuners, video playback, downloads, messaging and of course voice facilities all competing for that life. It is difficult to make solid predictions as to how batteries will develop as there are now so many competing new battery technologies each promising to significantly extend the life of mobile phones.

One of the real joys of the iPod is its intuitive, simple to use control menu system. With their screen and keys, phones tend to be pretty crowded and, in the short-term at least, it is hard to imagine a handset offering as elegant way for users to find their music. Rest assured though Sony Ericsson, Nokia et al are working on it.

Music playing phones
Are they the future?

What however will the music-playing phones look like? At the moment it is anyone's guess. Some analysts believe that the phone will develop into an uber gadget capable of displaying TV programmes, playing back video, taking high resolution images and blasting out music. Others believe that dedicated music phones will develop. They expect analogue of the Motorola E1000 which has a large screen for displaying tracks, and fairly powerful stereo speakers.

Death of the iPod?

In the last twelve months music playing on mobile phones has gone from being the preserve of just a few geeks to being serious option for all music lovers. But will its evolution of music playing handsets signal the death knell for the iPod?

The big question focuses on the issue of how many gadgets a person is prepared to carry. As PDA manufacturers have discovered to their cost Europeans and Asians don't enjoy toting bulging pockets full of gizmos, so mobile handset makers are already in a strong position. It is slightly different story in the US though with many gadget lovers happy to carry round bags full of electronic goodies.

If battery issues are resolved and a strong selection of music is made available to download on to a phone then the balance will tip in favour of the mobile. Quite how long this will take is anyone's guess, but it will be fascinating to watch it happen.

Storage; Flash or hard disk?

Storage isn't really an issue on mobile phones any more. Samsung has already kitted out one of its Korean mobiles, the SPH-V5400, with a 2.5 Gigabyte hard disk, while several Japanese companies are now parading one inch five Gigabyte hard disks. Nokia has also confirmed that its first mobile with a hard disk, the N91, will debut later this year. Hard disks offering as much as 10 or even 20 Gigabytes of storage could be integrated into mobile phones by the end of 2006.

Yet hard disks aren't the only option for phone manufacturers. The price of flash memory storage is also falling and it shouldn't be long before Secure

Right:
Motorola's MP3 playing phones are noted for excellent quality surround sound speakers.

Digital and Memory Stick cards capable of housing four Gigabytes of music are available at a reasonable price. This should be enough for all but the most die-hard music enthusiast.

In the long run, flash memory will probably win out as it will be cheaper and easier to produce than hard disks. Flash memory is also less of a drain on battery life than its hard disk rival and is obviously much smaller.

Download services; will they transfer?

For the phone to knock out the iPod the handset will need to be compatible with a download service that offers users tracks at the touch of button.

There are services available from several networks but so far many of the music services have used formats like AAC++, which are designed to be work with yesterday's GPRS phones rather than the storage rich 3G handsets of tomorrow.

Manufacturers and networks are now mulling over how far they can replicate the user experience of music to download to PCs on their mobile handset.

Motorola already has a tie in with Apple to use its iTunes music playing software on an upcoming phone. This will enable users who have downloaded the secure iTunes tracks in the AAC format to transfer them to a storage card and then play them back on the phone.

Motorola and several other manufactures are already toying with the idea of an iTunes download service where the handset would be able to grab full AAC tunes from the Apple website no matter where the users went. iTunes, and indeed its rivals Napster and Sony Connect, have a significantly larger library of songs than any of the European networks that are currently offering music downloads to phone services.

The one key hurdle for the industry is ensuring that digital rights management systems (DRMs) which works to stop piracy of the tunes, not only operates efficiently but doesn't impinge on the consumer's experience of downloading music. This is a tougher task than it sounds.

Music playing phones

Are they the future?

Music videos

Although much of the publicity and hype surrounding music on mobiles focuses on audio tracks, music videos could actually prove to be even more successful. 3G services in Europe and the US might relatively still be in nappies, but in Europe at least Vodafone and Orange have invested heavily in music video with growing archives of tracks ready to download.

Some analysts have suggested that music video downloads could hold the key for mobile phone companies as the generation under 25 are apparently more passionate about music with moving images than they are about plain audio. The development of mobile phone handsets to incorporate large screens (like the Nokia 7710) also enriches the users' experience of the video they are watching.

Innovations

One of the hottest mobile phone applications in the US at the moment is The Orb. This enables the user to stream whatever they have on their PC at home to their mobile. Although the service is mainly used to stream video or allow users to see work files, if

data prices drop then streaming audio from a server or PC in the home become a real possibility. The advantage for the user is that they don't need to clog up their phone's memory with music files.

Another innovation is music file swapping via Bluetooth or multimedia messaging. Already available in Spain via the Telefonica network, the service which has been pioneered by a company called Melodeo, allows users to send a track, or part of it to another phone. If the person who receives the track likes it and wants to keep it permanently they simply pay the network to buy it.

Finally one of the best mobile applications available in the UK is set to become even more useful during 2005. Shazam, which enables the user to identity any track they are listening to, will soon be offering users the chance to buy the track they have just heard.

After identifying a song the user simply clicks on a tag and then the download starts, they don't even need to know the name of the track.

The music playing phones

Nokia N91

The world's biggest cellphone manufacturer has been in and out of the music phone market over the last few years with some successful, and some rather unsuccessful, models. The N91 should change all that though. Set to go on sale in both the US and Europe in late 2005 the N91 is the first Nokia phone to boast an integrated hard disk – in this instance four Gigabytes. The N91 trounces rival music phones not just in storage, but also in terms of looks thanks to its elegant chocolate bar style design with music playing buttons that pull down to reveal the numeric keypad. The N91 boasts MP3 and AAC (though it isn't compatible with songs downloaded from the iTunes music store) playback, has a remote control in its accompanying earphones and features an FM tuner. Unlike many other phones it sports a 3.5mm headphone jack, so users can team up the handset with some seriously large cans if they fancy. Battery life is reasonable with the phone running for 12.5 hours as a music player. The hard disk is also shock proof, Nokia staff have apparently been throwing them around to test this, and the company is saying that

users can store up to 3000 tunes on the hard disk. The N91 will also play back AAC Plus files, which are used by European networks as over the air music downloads, and also has an audio out so you can hook it up to external speakers etc.

The phone has loads of other facilities including a two mega pixel camera, web browser, email, and, unusually for a phone of this size, integrated Wi-Fi. If users don't want to take two devices with them when leave their home then the Nokia N91 sounds like the gadget to have.

Sony Ericsson W600

The first of many Walkman music phones, we're told, the W800 cellphone is due in the third quarter of 2005. It has the Walkman logo on its fascia comes with a 512MB Sony Memory Stick Duo and has fifteen hours' battery life -- thirty if you play your music with the phone switched off. It will play back both MP3 and AAC files, but surprisingly not tracks made in Sony's own ATRAC format. There's also a 2-megapixel camera with a light designed in the same style of all Sony Ericsson handsets (i.e. so that it looks like a camera from the back and a phone at

Left:
The Nokia N91 features a four Gigabyte hard disk, which is the same size as the low-end version of the Apple iPod mini.

Music playing phones
Are they the future?

the front.) Sony Ericsson has paired it with Disk2Phone software for transferring files as well as high quality stereo headphones. Being able to use the music player with the handset switched off is an added bonus, and the Direct Music button lets you control the player independently of the phone.

Samsung E720

The Samsung E720 is the budget version of the MP3 playing phone. It has 88.5MB of memory (enough for around 30 songs) and can play music in MP3, AAC and AAC+ formats. It hooks up to your PC via USB for transfer of tracks. Its big USP though is that the phone has controls for the MP3 player on its fascia so when you to skip tracks or stop the music you don't have to open its clamshell.

Samsung SGH i300

Set to debut in the second half of 2005 the SGH i300 is a clear rival to Sony Ericsson/Motorola/Nokia music phones with its MP3/WMA player and storage for around sixty hours of tunes with its three gigabyte hard disk. Crucially Samsung had added a scroll navigation which wheel which the company says makes it easier to choose your music. The cellphone use Microsoft's smartphone operating system so as well as working seamlessly with Windows it also delivers cut down versions of applications like Word, Outlook and Internet Explorer.

Motorola iTunes phone

For the best part of a year Motorola and Apple have been working together on a cellphone that features Apple's iTunes software to enable playback of MP3 and AAC (including music downloaded from Apple's online music store site) files as well as delivering an easy to use interface. At the time of writing the phone hasn't yet been officially announced, but is likely to debut at some point during summer 2005. Motorola has already delivered a range of music playing phones like the E1000, which are noted for excellent MP3 players and good quality, for a cellphone, stereo speakers. In Europe, and to a lesser extent in the US, there is some hostility to the concept of the iTunes phone as many carriers have their own music download services which in effect are rivals to the Apple iTunes music store.
Given recent announcements from Samsung and Nokia over the launch of their hard disk music phones, it will be interesting to see if the Motorola handset has flash or hard disk memory.

Left:
Samsung's E720 is a
budget cell with music
playing facilities.

CHAPTER 19

Personal media players

Video, images & music

The next step in the digital evolution is the personal media player. Here we look at Microsoft's contribution, and the range of portable video players on the market. We'll also get to grips with transferring video files onto your media player and recording programmes from television and ask is it legal to rip DVDs?

Personal media players
Video, images & music

With the advent of the music playing hard drive, it didn't take long for manufacturers to realize that music wasn't the only format suited to this medium. Portable entertainment systems had been tried before, but with little success. In the early 90s Sony introduced its Watchman, a small LCD panel that featured an integrated TV tuner.

However consumers weren't impressed by a poor quality screen, below par picture and the fact that new batteries were required almost every half hour.

But with the success of the digital music player, manufacturers once again began to explore the potential of portable video products. Even in the early stages of digital music players companies such as Archos we're delivering hard drive music jukeboxes with small color screens capable of playing back digital video.

And it wasn't too long before larger-screened devices were appearing that were better suited to movie playback, offering users the opportunity to watch movies and recorded TV shows on the move.

Thomson and Archos were two companies leading the way in the early stages, but other manufacturers didn't take long to follow.

Then Microsoft got in on the act, releasing a portable version of its Media Center operating system. Media Center had been designed as part of Microsoft's plans for more integrated, multimedia households and the OS effectively turned PCs into home entertainment systems for watching TV, recording TV and playing back music.

The launch of Portable version meant that people could now add those features to smaller handheld devices, and a number of new units have sprung up from a selection of manufacturers. Although they all

Right:
Creative's Microsoft powered Zen Media Center is one of the most popular personal video players on sale.

offer a selection of different designs, Microsoft-based systems are united by a common user interface, as well as the ever present home key and certain minimum specifications that Microsoft has insisted upon.

Digital files

The digital video portable media players contain isn't stored in the original format because files would be far too large. Instead, the devices convert the video into formats like MPEG4 or Windows Media. Just as with digital music files like MP3s and WMAs, this conversion process compresses files so they are reduced in size sufficiently to fit on the player's hard drive. Invariably, this process reduces image quality along the way and you will find that digital films on your media player can't match the quality of standard digital video

Although video is the headline feature of the Portable Media Centers (PMCs) and non-Windows players, these devices also play back music and display JPEG picture images that have been transferred to the player from a PC.

Slow uptake

But while these sorts of players have been around for a while, their popularity is still a long way behind that of the digital music players. And there's nowhere near the number of manufacturers entering products into the fray as there is into the digital music market. There are many reasons for that, cost being probably the most obvious, and the most important explanation. It may be relatively easy to create a flash player, or a basic hard drive player to rival the established giants of the music market, but coming up with a workable model for the portable media player market is far harder to achieve on a tight budget. If manufacturers don't

Personal media players
Video, images & music

want to pay to license Microsoft's Media Center software, they'll need to come up with a workable user interface to run their player on. Then there's the problem of making a hard drive that's large enough to store a decent amount of media data, large enough to incorporate a decent-sized, high quality screen, but small enough to make carrying it around a realistic option.

There has also been a problem of trying to establish if the buying public even wants gadgets like these. It's a commonly held belief by some of the more skeptical manufacturers that people want portable entertainment that will go on in the background as they go about their day.

Having to focus on a TV show or movie when you're out and about may be too much of a demand on our attention, especially if we're trying to do something else such as commute into work.

There's no doubt that many of us would be grateful of the diversion of a favorite TV show or film when we're trying to pass a boring journey, or when we're stuck waiting somewhere, but the majority of people will end up using their media players to listen to music for the bulk of their time.

And this presents a further problem. Even with the very latest and slimmest handhelds, the players are still currently too large and cumbersome to carry with you everywhere. It's more likely that most people would only take them out with them when they know that they're going to have the spare time in their day to focus their attention on their portable media player.

This means that, for many people, there's just no point in investing the extra money into a bulkier player that they will only use for digital video on the odd occasion and will simply want to play music on in the interim periods.

The large memory capacities of some (though not all) players may be enough of a selling point, but that's counter-balanced with a battery life that's usually far shorter lived than standard music hard drives – even those with color screens.

Finally, confusion about how to get digital video loaded onto players, and concerns about just how legal that saved video content actually is, has meant that many manufacturers are still steering clear, and many consumers are remaining unmoved by the new digital multimedia centers.

Legality issues

If you've ever looked into the methods for ripping DVDs into digital formats that a media center can play back, you'll know how hard it is to find the information you're after. That's because ripping DVDs is actually illegal – even if you bought the DVD yourself, simply want to rip it for personal use, and have no intention of showing it or distributing it to the public. Unless these copyright issues are addressed, it's best to steer clear of copying your DVDs to your hard drive player. Some companies are claiming that ripping your DVDs to watch on your portable player constitutes "fair use", but until the law becomes less murky – and one of the larger software companies such as Microsoft start supplying ripping software – it's safer to steer clear.

You can, however, download films to your hard drive from legal online movie download stores. You're also allowed to record TV shows onto your computer to copy across to your player, and if a film was is on television, there's no harm in recording it to watch on your media player – so long as you don't archive it on there indefinitely. And, of course, you're perfectly within your rights to copy your own home movies onto your player, converting them into digital format without any concerns for copyright infringement.

Below:
French maker Archos was one of the pioneers of the personal video player. It has several models in its range

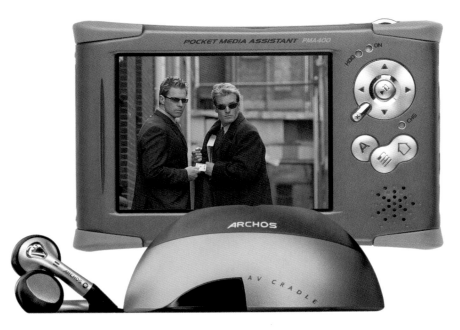

Personal media players
Video, images & music

Finding digital content

Locating digital movie download sites is certainly not as straightforward as you might imagine. There may be abundant supplies of digital music stores, but movies are another matter altogether. Many of the big movie studios seem reluctant to allow stores to sell digital files of their films to download – something that surely must change in the future. Record companies have suffered the same initial reluctance, but now many of them have begun to see the benefits in providing their content to online music retailers, and some even include a digital version of the album on the CD content. Just how long it will be before the movie studios start including portable player versions of the movies on DVDs remains to be seen, but if they follow the lead of the record labels, it hopefully won't be long before they wake up to the potential of online digital content sales.

But all is not completely hopeless for the digital movie market. Probably the largest company selling legal video downloads is CinemaNow. It has a large selection of digital content, a fair proportion of which you can download to your player to own and watch as many times as you like. While there is a very broad selection of genres and certificate ratings, many of the largest box office movies are still missing from the catalogue. This is simply due to the resistance of the largest movie studios, and if you want to watch the latest summer blockbusters or your favorite comedy, you may have to wait until you can record a live television broadcast.

Recording from the television

Being able to watch recordings of live broadcasts on your handheld media player is one of its most appealing features. But just how do you get the data onto the player? Some of the units, such as the Archos models are capable of recording shows directly from the television – plug them into your set and the player will encode the show, making it compressed enough to save onto the hard drive. However, many of the Windows Media Centers, such as Creative's Zen Portable Media Center, are unable to encode directly from a live broadcast source. In those cases, you will need to record shows onto your computer – usually best done on a Windows Media Center PC or any other computer that includes a TV tuner.

Once that's done, data can be transferred via USB to your player. If you already have the technology in place to do this, it's not too much of an extra chore to send programs to your player in this way, but those without the correct set up should be aware that they may have to purchase extra items to get their system working.Increasing numbers of new players being launched now offer TV Tuners built into the multimedia hard drives.

Windows Media Centers

One of the first players to launch running the Windows Portable Media Center was the Creative Zen Portable Media Center.

This player provides space for up to 85 hours of movies, recorded TV programs or home videos on its 20GB hard drive. Alternatively, you can squeeze on up to 9000 tunes, or store and view tens of thousands of JPEG digital photos.

There's a set of built in speakers for sharing your music and movies with others, or you can connect up some headphones for private viewings. Battery life is quoted at 7 hours, so you should get through a couple of movies before the screen goes dark. Your recorded shows and downloaded movies will need to be transferred to your player via the USB 2.0 connection from your computer. Samsung's silver YH-999 is a small, good looking player that has room for up to 80 hours of video content, or up to 5000 tunes on its 20GB hard drive.

Data is transferred via the USB 2.0 connection, and you can listen out loud on the speakers, or using the supplied earphones.

Personal media players
Video, images & music

Other Portable Video Players

Digital Square is a Korean company selling the PMP1000 through a number of resellers in the West. The sleek silver handheld is a 20GB hard disk personal video player with a 3.5-inch color screen. It supports direct coding for MP3s (but not video content) and comes with an unusual touch screen interface. It also includes a recordable FM radio, voice recorder, photo album viewer, a calculator and a dictionary.

Archos' AV400 Pocket Video Recorder is among the most highly specified portable players on the market. With models going up to 100GB capacities, you'll be able to store an awful lot of multimedia content onto your player. A big bonus is that you can record TV shows and movies directly from a TV, VCR or cable/satellite receiver using the supplied docking cradle. You can also set up a recording scheduler that will record shows automatically from television just like a full-size hard drive recorder. Obviously, you also get support for music files – MP3, WMA (included DRM protected files) and WAV file types will all work – plus a JPEG photo viewer and the facility to transfer images straight onto your

player from a digital camera. The range includes a number of add-on products, such as the FM radio box, making this a player offering plenty of choice. But all this comes at a price – battery life for movie playback is only quoted at 3 hours.

Just as it did with previous models, Archos has also added video playback capabilities to its smaller music jukebox range.

The Gmini 400 is a 20GB hard disk music player that can also play video. While the small size of the 2.2-inch color screen isn't going to give you the best playback experience, it does mean that those who don't want the larger PVPs have the option of this smaller alternative.

The price is also more in keeping with other hard drive music players, making it a cost-effective solution. Other features include: support for MP3, WMA (DRM and ID3 tags enabled) and WAV music files; album cover art display on the color LCD; voice recorder with built-in mic; photo viewer; and a built in Compact Flash card reader for expanding memory and transferring digital images and files.

Right:
NHJ's MPM-202 comes
with a cradles that
includes a TV tuner.

Left:
Digital Square's PMP
1000 sports a 20
Gigabyte hard disk and a
3.5 inch color screen.

Other players worth checking out are NHJ-MPM 202
and Mustek's 40GB PVR H140. The MPM 202
includes a TV Tuner on the cradle so you can watch
live television. It comes in 30GB and 60GB capacities
and will encode straight from DVDs and VHS
videotapes as well as live television. There's also slots
for Secure Digital and Compact Flash memory cards.
Mustek's PVR H140 comes with direct TV recording
and a digital voice recorder, as well as all the
standard multimedia facilities.

Internet radio stations

Online radio

The digital music revolution isn't all about MP3 players. Hundreds of radio stations transmit over the net and tuning in to their broadcasts is a very simple process. Here's how you do it.

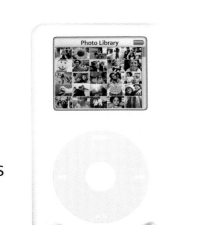

You might not know it but you already own one of the most fantastic radio tuners ever devised. Not only can it pull down signals from thousands of radio stations across the globe, it can also give you a second chance to hear programs that were recorded days ago. The tuner is of course your PC.

Internet radio is simply a description of the thousands of websites that stream audio signals across the web. Some Internet radio stations are versions of existing stations that are also transmitted over FM or MW. Others are small time operations that give enthusiasts a global platform for the music that they cherish.

There is an astonishing choice of stations with almost every country in the world, and every genre of music, represented.

Tuning-in is relatively simple. You can hear Internet radio stations even if you only have a dial-up Internet connection, although this however does limit the choice to those stations which broadcast in lower-quality audio. With a broadband connection you can tune-in and leave your station permanently connected just as you would with a traditional FM/MW radio station.

As well as an Internet connection you'll also need audio software. Your computer, no matter if it is a PC or a Mac, will have this already built in. For PC-owners it is Windows Media while for Mac users it is iTunes. In both instances you simply click on the radio icon and you'll be presented with a choice of stations.

For Windows Media there will be a listing of the most popular (NPR, BBC 6 Music, Virgin Radio, BBC World Service etc) plus an option of searching for stations either by genre or actually inputting the name of the broadcaster. If you know the station's URL (website address) you can just key that into Internet Explorer/Netscape and click on the listen icon on the page.

You aren't limited to just the audio software that comes on you computer. Many net radio enthusiasts swear by the latest version of the Real – Real Player

Internet radio stations
Online radio

10 (www.real.com), which has a good selection of stations, many of which are advert-free and boast good quality audio. The BBC uses a free version of the Real player which can be downloaded via www.bbc.co.uk. If you still can't find the station you are looking for, there are many radio search engines which display broadcaster via the content they play and their location.

So what do Internet Radio stations sound like? You may have heard that they deliver music and speech in poor sound quality. This is a half-truth. Some stations use compressed audio formats, but they are free of the crack and hiss that dog medium wave and some FM broadcasts.

Stations also transmit at different data rates which impacts on the quality of the audio that's delivered. The basic rate is usually 32kbps, which delivers poor quality sound, but can be heard on dial-up connections. Faster data rates of 64kbps, or even as high as 128kbps, deliver better quality sound. Although it must be conceded that even at this top rate the sound quality is in no way a rival for high-end audio formats like CD and SACD.

Another wonderful feature of Internet radio is the way in which some stations allow listeners to say goodbye to the schedules and listen to programs whenever they want to. The BBC is especially good at offering re-runs of the most popular programs from all of its stations. Annoyingly though not all its programs can be streamed in this way and, for copyright reasons, many are only available for a couple of weeks after their first broadcast. Another bonus is that by using tools like Audio Hijack (www.rogueamoeba.com/audiohijack/) you can actually record Internet radio programs saving them to your PC. You can then burn them onto a CD to listen to on the move or even port them on to a music player like an iPod.

Once you have sampled the delights of Internet radio you'll probably wish that you could listen to it in every room of the house. The simple way of doing this is to create a home network, preferably a wireless one.

This will allow any PC you have in your home to share your broadband Internet connection and obviously access Internet radio. If you have a laptop that has wireless (or Wi-Fi or 802.11b) facilities either built in or added via a PCMCIA card you can listen to Internet radio via the PC's speaker, or – much better – plug it into your home stereo via a jack-to-phono lead.

There are also a range of devices that allow users to tune into Internet radio via wireless connections.

Finally if you have a broadband connection, a big CD collection, a couple of hours to spare and a few pounds a month to spend you can set up your own Internet radio station. Check out the excellent website Live 365 (www.live365.com), which acts as your personal broadcaster. You simply upload your MP3 music files to your site (this is the bit that takes a few hours), choose the order you want your tracks to be heard and then press play. Live 365 does the rest and your music can be listened to by anyone with an Internet connection. More ambitious jocks can even broadcast live and introduce the tracks. Watch out Howard Stern and Chris Moyles!

Below:
Live 365 (www.live365.com) is an innovative online service that enables anyone with a computer to create their own internet radio station

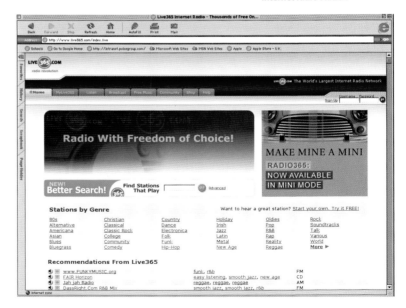

CHAPTER 21

The future

What's next?

In the final chapter we explain why video to go is the future, and ask how long MP3 will be around. We will also help you to pipe music around your home.

So what will tomorrow's digital music player look like? Will it be tiny, yet boast lots of storage? Or will it be larger with a screen for watching video? Or will it not exist at all and in fact be shoehorned into a cellphone?

Video to go

The answer is in fact yes to all three. No one can say for certain which way digital audio will develop but chances are the market will splinter in the three ways outlined above.

Much really depends on how both Americans and Europeans take to the idea of a music playing cellphone. If they catch on in Europe especially, it could signal the end of many different types of music players. However, unlike Europeans who tend to prefer all their gadgets in one device, Americans seem happy to take more than one gizmo around with them. So don't write off the music player just yet.

What's likely to happen is that music players will not actually get a great deal smaller - they are arguably already at the limit of usability.

Instead manufacturers will offer more storage, so as flash memory prices continue to drop, five or even ten Gigabyte players the size of today's one Gigabyte models will become available.

At the other end of the audio-playing market larger hard disk units will still exist, but these could end up being as much about video and image playback as they are about music. What could really accelerate take up of those media players is if a dominant video format emerges which the manufacturers and software companies are convinced is copyright secure. So for example they can use it to offer movies which users then download online and then transfer to their player. At the moment Microsoft is hoping that Windows Media will become the key format, though DiVx is popular too and quite possibly another format will emerge.

Another possibility is that digital audio players will in fact be superseded by a games console. Sony's PlayStation Portable (PSP), which debuted in the US in the spring of 2005 and launches in Europe later this year, has extremely good music and video playback features. Some critics have already dubbed it the Walkman of the twenty first century.

The future
What's next

Music round the home

After changing the way we listen to music on the move digital audio will soon transform the way we listen to music at home too. More and more manufacturers are offering devices that take the music stored on a computer and then enabling the user to pipe them (the technical term is streaming) to hi-fi systems around the home. These range from very swish looking high-end hi-fi oriented systems like the Wireless Music Center from Philips, and the Sonos Digital Music system, to basic add-ons for games consoles and PCs like Microsoft's Media Center Extender. Apple already has a product, AirPort Express, which enables users to wirelessly stream music around their home.

Even if you don't fancy a full-on wireless system – which incidentally is a lot easier to set up than they sound – you can still listen to the music on your iPod or MP3 player in other areas of the house. Simply connecting the player to the hi-fi via its line out socket will enable you to pipe the digital music through your home system. Alternatively one type of mini system that is growing very popular is the recharging speaker unit for the iPod like Altec Lansing's. As well as powering and pepping up the player's battery these devices also include speakers so you can listen to the music. Most will also fold up so they are compact enough to fit into a bag so you can take them away with you.

Lastly if you thought you'd seen every possible device now featuring an MP3 player think again. On the day the book went to press PalmOne, creators of PDAs (personal digital assistant), unveiled a new organizer with a hard disk aimed at customers who wanted lots of storage to keep MP3 and video files as well as their Word documents. And there will be plenty of other devices to follow.

And what about MP3?

So much for the hardware… But what will happen to the various music formats? Will MP3 still rule the roost in a decade's time or will it have been superseded by a better quality format?

It really is hard to say at the moment. MP3 has succeeded because of its popularity with

Conclusion

consumers, not because of any backing from the music industry; in fact attempts by software companies to foist new formats on customers have largely been unsuccessful. However MP3 is already starting to look like an ageing format. In terms of sound quality there are many better and more efficient formats available. What matters most is that a format emerges that maintains the excellent sound quality of the original recording – or the CDs if it's taken direct – yet is small enough not to take up too much space on devices. Some critics are confident that a format like Apple's Lossless, which offers a significantly superior performance to MP3 will emerge as the winner. Others aren't quite so sure. While the existing formats might not be ideal, they work well enough for most people.

So how does this impact on your buying decision? Well it shouldn't at all. Most of the players you are considering buying only have a shelf life of two to three years anyhow. If you buy an MP3 playing cellphone that lifespan may even be shorter. So while it is good to try and guess what the future holds, don't let it stop you from buying the player you want now.

Hopefully this book will have given you a good idea as to which players are available. Do remember though that your decision might not be completely based around hardware.

The music download service you opt for can have a significant impact on your choice of player too. So if you are already downloading iTunes tracks you need an Apple player. For Napster try a Creative, Samsung or Rio device and for Connect go for Sony.

Which ever model you chose though here's to some great tunes…